HOUGH

California
Science

Interactive
Text

HOUGHTON MIFFLIN   BOSTON

Printed in the U.S.A.

ISBN 13: 978-0-547-00468-6
ISBN 10: 0-547-00468-0

16   0928   16 15

4500520038

Contents

WHAT DO YOU KNOW?

Earth is your home planet. How much do you know about it?

What is Earth's major source of energy?

_____

What material is found inside Earth?

_____

_____

What are two features found on Earth's surface?

_____

_____

Earth's Structure

Contents

WHAT DO YOU WANT TO KNOW?

What do you want to find out about the inside of Earth?

_____

_____

What do you want to find out about how scientists map Earth's surface?

_____

_____

What else do you want to know about Earth's structure?

_____

_____

VOCABULARY

revolution a complete orbit around an object, such as the Sun *(noun)*

rotation a complete turn about an axis *(noun)*

VOCABULARY SKILL: Word Parts

Look at the word *rotation*. This word is made up of the root word *rotate*, which means "to turn," and the suffix *-tion*, which means "the act of." Use this information to write your own definition of the word *rotation*.

What Makes Earth a Special Planet?

The Sun is the main source of energy for Earth. Different places on Earth have different amounts of solar energy.

A Special Planet

Earth is the third planet from the Sun. All the planets get energy from the Sun. But Earth is the only planet where living things grow.

There are many reasons why Earth is special. Earth is the only planet that has liquid water. Water is important for life on Earth. Liquid water covers about 70 percent of Earth's surface!

Earth contains the perfect conditions to support life.

Look at the photo of Earth on page 4. It was taken from space. The blue color comes from Earth's oceans. The white swirls are clouds.

Earth's gravity is strong. Gravity pulls on Earth's atmosphere. The atmosphere is the air that surrounds the planet. Currents of air in Earth's atmosphere keep temperatures mild, which means it is not too hot and not too cold.

The atmosphere is made up of nitrogen, oxygen, and small amounts of other gases. Earth's atmosphere and magnetic field protect the planet. Earth's thin rocky outer layer is called the crust. All living things live on the crust.

You can find more Earth facts in the table.

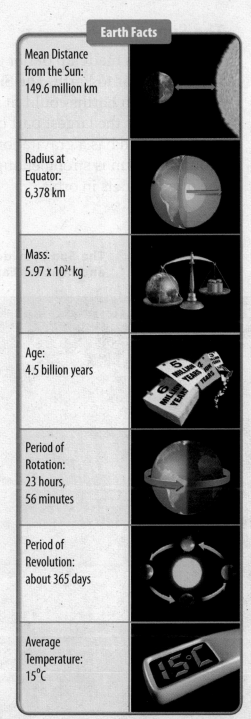

Earth Facts

Mean Distance from the Sun: 149.6 million km	
Radius at Equator: 6,378 km	
Mass: 5.97×10^{24} kg	
Age: 4.5 billion years	
Period of Rotation: 23 hours, 56 minutes	
Period of Revolution: about 365 days	
Average Temperature: 15°C	

1. Earth is a special planet. It is the only planet we know of on which living things are found. Tell how each of these items helps support life.

   a. liquid water: _____

   _____

   b. gravity: _____

   _____

   c. atmosphere: _____

   _____

   _____

2. Where do all living things live on Earth?

   _____

3. What is the star closest to Earth called?

_____

4. What effect does the Sun's gravity have on Earth?

_____

5. What two things does the Sun provide to Earth?

a. _____

b. _____

The Sun

The Sun is made up of hot gas called plasma. It is the closest star to Earth. The Sun is so large that more than 1 million Earths could fit inside it!

The Sun is the largest part of the solar system. Like Earth, the Sun has a gravitational pull. The gravity around the Sun is strong enough to keep Earth and the other planets in orbit.

The Sun provides light and heat for Earth.

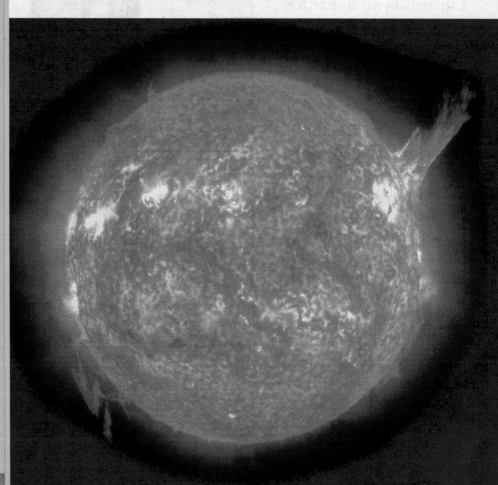

6

Sun Facts	
Diameter	1,390,000 km
Mass	2.0×10^{30} kg
Surface Temperature	5,500°C
Core Temperature	15,000,000°C
Composition	74% hydrogen 24% helium 2% other elements
Age	4.6 billion years

As you can see in the table above, the Sun is very, very hot. It gives off a huge amount of energy that moves through space. A small amount of that energy comes to Earth and heats Earth's air, land, and water.

The Sun is the main source of energy for Earth. There would be no life on Earth without the Sun. Sun, water, and weather work together to support life. Plants need energy from the Sun to grow. Plants provide food for people and other living things.

6. List three things that the Sun's energy heats on Earth.

a. _____

b. _____

c. _____

7. What is the main source of energy for Earth?

_____

_____

I Wonder . . . What does the Sun's energy have to do with the foods you eat?

_____

_____

_____

_____

_____

8. Look at the picture of day and night. Think about Earth spinning west to east on its axis. Label *west* and *east* on the diagram. Then draw an arrow on the diagram that shows the direction that Earth turns as it rotates.

9. Look again at the diagram. How do you know that most of North America is facing the Sun?

_____

_____

Day and Night

The Sun seems to move across the sky every day. It is really Earth that is moving. Earth rotates from west to east on its axis.

The axis is an imaginary line that passes through the North and South poles. Each full **rotation**, or complete turn on the axis, takes one day. The half of Earth facing the Sun is in daytime. The other half of Earth is dark and it is nighttime.

day   night

A sundial tells time with sunlight and shadows.

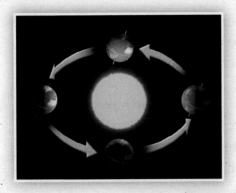

REVOLUTION
A revolution is a complete orbit around an object, such as the Sun.

ROTATION
A rotation is a complete turn about an axis.

The Year and the Seasons

Earth travels around the Sun. As you know, it takes Earth one year to complete one revolution. A **revolution** is the full circle that Earth makes around the Sun.

Why do we have seasons on Earth? Earth rotates on its axis. The axis is tilted and Earth is at an angle. Sometimes the Northern Hemisphere is tilted toward the Sun. The sunlight makes it warmer, so it is spring or summer. It is fall or winter in the Southern Hemisphere.

At other times during the year, the Southern Hemisphere tilts toward the Sun. Then the Southern Hemisphere is warmer and is in spring or summer. It is fall or winter in the Northern Hemisphere.

10. Use the cause-and-effect chart to compare and contrast rotation and revolution.

Causes		Effects
Earth rotates on its axis.	→	_____ _____ _____
Earth revolves around the Sun.	→	_____ _____ _____

11. Earth has seasons because the planet rotates on a tilted axis. Use the table below to describe seasons in the Northern Hemisphere.

Position of Northern Hemisphere	Temperature	Length of Day	Seasons
Tilted toward the Sun			
Tilted away from the Sun			

12. What seasons occur in the Southern Hemisphere when the Northern Hemisphere is having spring and summer?

_____

In the middle of the year, the Northern Hemisphere tilts towards the Sun. The days are longer and the weather is warmer. This causes the seasons of spring and summer.

During the rest of the year, the Northern Hemisphere tilts away from the Sun. The Sun is lower in the sky. Days are shorter. This causes the cooler seasons of fall and winter.

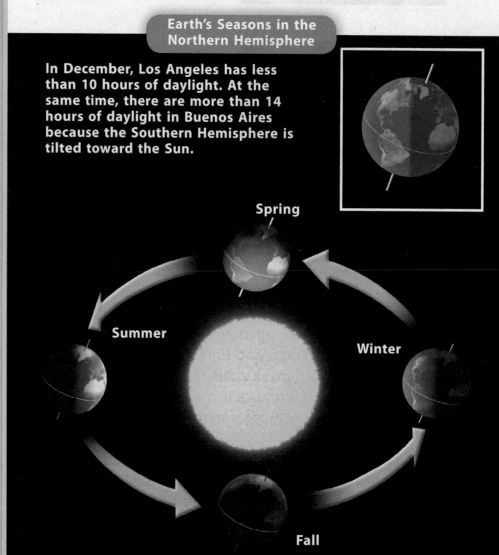

Earth's Seasons in the Northern Hemisphere

In December, Los Angeles has less than 10 hours of daylight. At the same time, there are more than 14 hours of daylight in Buenos Aires because the Southern Hemisphere is tilted toward the Sun.

Spring

Summer

Winter

Fall

Steady temperatures make Earth a good home for all living things—including you.

Earth's Climates

The solar energy the Sun provides for Earth does not change very much. It stays about the same over hundreds of years. This means that the climate, or weather over time, can be predicted. People know what kind of weather to expect in different places at different times of year.

For example, the average temperature in Chicago is about -6°C (22°F) every January. As you go south, it gets warmer. The average temperature in Houston is 11°C (52°F) in January.

13. Why can climate, or weather over time, be predicted?

_____

_____

_____

I Wonder . . . Write what you think would happen to seasons and climate if Earth suddenly moved more slowly in its orbit?

_____

_____

_____

_____

_____

_____

14. List two ways that location causes areas to have different temperatures and climates.

a. _____

_____

_____

b. _____

_____

_____

McWay Cove is near the Pacific coast in central California. The Pacific Ocean and the southern location keep this area warm all year.

What causes the different temperatures? Cities in the southern United States are closer to the equator so they get more solar energy. This solar energy makes them warmer.

Other factors affect climate. Oceans affect the temperature of cities along the coast. This is why California cities have warmer weather in the winter than places farther inland.

Earth's Future

Earth has changed over the years. Scientists study the ways humans are changing Earth. From them we can learn how to protect the planet.

In the 1970s, scientists discovered the side effects of certain chemicals. These chemicals were called chlorofluorocarbons, or CFCs. They were destroying the ozone layer. The ozone layer is part of the upper atmosphere. It protects Earth from the Sun's ultraviolet rays. The chemicals that were harming the ozone layer are now banned.

Earth is the only home that people have. Taking care of it is a job for everyone.

15. Complete the sequence chart detailing the events that led to the banning of CFCs.

> CFCs were used in some products.

↓

> _____
> _____
> _____
> _____

↓

> CFCs were banned.

Summary   The Sun is the major source of energy for Earth. Different areas on Earth receive different amounts of solar energy. What season is it in California when the Northern Hemisphere is tilted away from the Sun?

 Cause and Effect   What keeps Earth in orbit around the Sun?

Cause	Effect
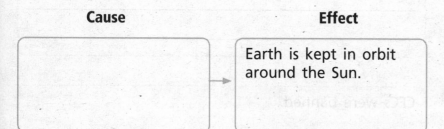	Earth is kept in orbit around the Sun.

Recycle plastics, metals, and paper to conserve Earth's resources.

Scientists study other human activities that affect the planet. People burn fossil fuels, cut down forests, and catch too many fish in certain areas. These activities could have a lasting effect on Earth. You will learn more about these issues as you read on.

Every day, you make choices that affect Earth's future. Learning about Earth will help you to choose wisely.

CAUSE AND EFFECT

What keeps Earth in orbit around the Sun?

14

What Is Earth's Structure?

Earth is made up of different layers. Each layer is special and different from the others.

Hot Inside

In some places on Earth, hot water shoots up from the ground. This water fountain is called a geyser (GUY.zuhr). Geysers come from deep inside Earth. The hot water tells us that Earth is hot inside.

One place that has many geysers and hot springs is Yellowstone National Park. At Yellowstone, visitors see the signs of Earth's hot center. But just how hot is it inside Earth?

A geyser shoots a stream of hot water into the air.

VOCABULARY

asthenosphere the plastic part of the mantle beneath the lithosphere *(noun)*

core the innermost layer of Earth, which extends to the center of Earth *(noun)*

crust the outermost layer of Earth *(noun)*

lithosphere the rigid shell formed by the upper mantle and the crust *(noun)*

mantle the solid layer just below Earth's crust *(noun)*

VOCABULARY SKILL: Word Origins

Astheno- comes from the Greek word *asthenes*, meaning "weak." The word *sphere* comes from the Greek word *sphaira*, which means "ball." Write a definition for *asthenosphere* based on the meanings of the original Greek words.

_____

_____

 1.b. Students know that Earth is made up of several layers.

1. List three things that scientists study that help them learn about the inside of Earth.

   a. _____

   b. _____

   c. _____

2. Use your finger to trace the temperature line on the graph. How does the temperature of Earth's center compare with the temperature at the surface?

   _____

   _____

Hot springs, geysers, and mudpots are signs that Earth is hot inside.

Scientists study the inside of Earth to find its temperature. They drill holes in the crust. But scientists cannot drill to the center of Earth. Geysers and volcanoes show scientists what Earth is like inside.

Scientists also study the movement of Earth after an earthquake. This movement is measured in waves, called seismic waves. The study of seismic waves inside Earth can also tell scientists about temperature.

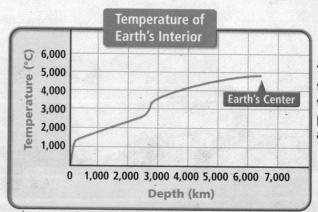

Temperature of Earth's Interior

Earth's Center

This graph shows that it is hotter at the center of the planet than it is at Earth's crust.

Earth's Layers

Earth has many layers. Some are made of solid rock. Others are made of different metals. The **crust** is the outer layer of Earth. It is thinner than the other layers. It is made of solid rock.

There is a solid layer under Earth's crust. This layer is called the **mantle**. The mantle is denser than the crust. This means the rock is packed together even tighter. The upper mantle and crust form a hard shell called the **lithosphere** (LITH oh sfir).

This canyon shows the layers of rock in Earth's crust.

3. List the names of the two upper layers of Earth. Then write a description of each layer.

   a. _____

   _____

   _____

   b. _____

   _____

   _____

4. What do scientists call the hard shell formed by the crust and the upper mantle?

   _____

5. The lower part of the mantle is called the

_____.

Describe how this layer of rock moves.

_____

_____

_____

6. Describe the two parts of Earth's core.

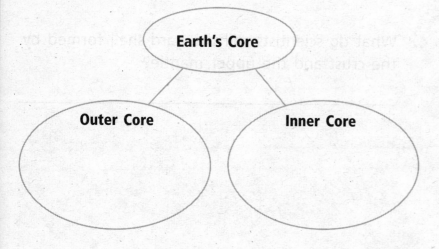

Under the lithosphere the rock is much softer. This rock can flow slowly, like melted plastic. The plastic part of the mantle under the lithosphere is called the **asthenosphere** (as THEN uh sfir).

The **core** is at the center of Earth. The core has two layers, the outer core and the inner core. The outer core is the only layer that is liquid. The inner core is thick and very hot. The pressure from the outer layers keeps it from melting.

You can picture Earth like a peach or other fruit with a thin skin and a pit in the center.

Imagine this peach is Earth. The peach pit is like the inner core.

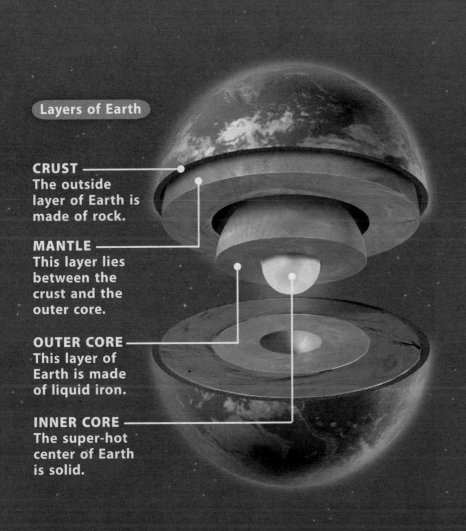

Layers of Earth

CRUST
The outside layer of Earth is made of rock.

MANTLE
This layer lies between the crust and the outer core.

OUTER CORE
This layer of Earth is made of liquid iron.

INNER CORE
The super-hot center of Earth is solid.

7. Use the clues to identify each of Earth's layers.

Clue	Layer
Outside layer of Earth, made of solid rock	
Layer between the crust and core	
Layer made of liquid iron	
Super-hot solid center of Earth	

I Wonder . . . The temperature of Earth's inner core is similar to the temperature of the Sun's surface. With a temperature that high, what keeps the inner core from melting? What do you think?

_____

_____

_____

_____

_____

19

8. Look at the picture on this page. Trace some of the magnetic field lines with your finger. Then draw a small doughnut on the diagram to show where Earth's magnetic field is generated.

I Wonder . . . Earth's magnetic field is much like the field around a bar magnet. Use the diagram to help you explain this idea.

_____

_____

_____

_____

_____

_____

Earth's Magnetic Field

Have you ever used a compass? A compass works because Earth has a magnetic field. Earth has a north magnetic pole and a south magnetic pole.

Earth has a magnetic field because of the outer core. Scientists have found that the outer core contains iron. The movement of the liquid iron in the outer core creates electric currents that form the magnetic field.

A magnetic field is around Earth.

Auroras are usually seen near the North and South poles.

Earth's magnetic field has changed direction many times over millions of years. This fact helps scientists explain how continents move.

Humans and other living things on Earth are protected by the magnetic field. Solar wind sends electrically charged particles to Earth. These particles crash into materials in Earth's atmosphere. When this happens, beautiful lights flash across the sky. These lights are called auroras.

COMPARE AND CONTRAST

How is Earth like a peach? How is it different?

Summary   Earth is made up of different layers. Each layer has it own characteristics. List three characteristics of Earth you learned in this lesson.

a. _____

_____

b. _____

_____

c. _____

_____

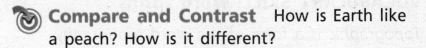
Compare and Contrast   How is Earth like a peach? How is it different?

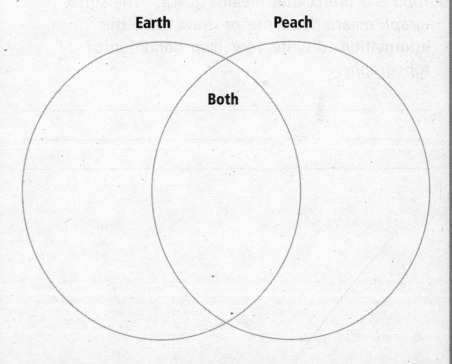

Earth   Peach

Both

21

VOCABULARY

contour lines lines on a topographic map that connect points with the same elevation *(noun)*

elevation height above sea level *(noun)*

topographic map a map that shows the shape of surface features and their elevations *(noun)*

VOCABULARY SKILL: Word Forms

Topographic is a form of the word *topography*. *Topo* is a prefix that means "place." The suffix *-graph* means "to write or draw." Use this information to write your own definition of *topography*.

_____

_____

_____

7.f. Read topographic and geologic maps and interpret a scale map.

3 What Makes Up Earth's Surface?

The surface of Earth includes water and land. Surface features have different locations, shapes, and elevations.

A Watery Planet

Most of Earth's surface is covered by oceans. Oceans are large bodies of salt water. All of Earth's oceans are connected. They form one world ocean.

Huge landmasses that rise above the ocean surface are called continents. Lakes and rivers on the continents hold fresh water. Fresh water does not have salt in it.

Plants, humans, and other animals need fresh water to live, but very little of Earth's water is fresh. This makes fresh water an important resource.

Earth's Surface

Freshwater 2%
- Glaciers
- Ground Water
- Rivers and Lakes

Salt Water 69%

Land 29%

California's Highs and Lows

Sea Level
0m

Mount Whitney
4,418m

Death Valley
-86m

Land Features

Mountains are the tallest landform on Earth. They have steep slopes and high peaks. Hills are smaller than mountains. Their rounded tops stand above the land.

Mountain valleys are long, narrow areas of land between mountains or hills. Very deep valleys with steep sides are called canyons.

Plateaus are areas of land that are high and flat. Plateaus are usually near the tops of canyons. The flat land of a plateau can stretch for miles.

1. What covers Earth's surface?

    a. _____

    b. _____

2. Look back at your answer to question 1. Circle the material that covers most of Earth's surface.

3. Look at the graph. List three sources of freshwater.

    a. _____

    b. _____

    c. _____

4. Tell how mountains and valleys are related.

    _____

    _____

    _____

5. Compare and contrast plains and plateaus.

Plains and Plateaus

Plains **Plateaus**

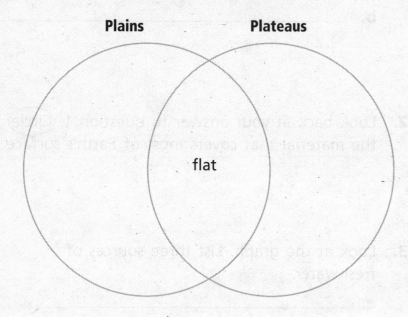

flat

6. List three places plains are found.

a. _____

b. _____

c. _____

Plains are also flat, but they are lower than plateaus. Many states in the Midwest region of the United States are made up of plains.

A flood plain is a different kind of plain. It is an area of flat land on both sides of a river. The flood plain is covered with water when a river overflows.

Beaches are flat areas of land next to an ocean or large lake. You will learn more about beaches in the next chapter.

RIVER VALLEYS These are between mountains and hills. They can also be found on plains.

COASTAL PLAINS These are low-lying areas. They are near the ocean's shore.

The small circles on this map stand for hills.

San Francisco

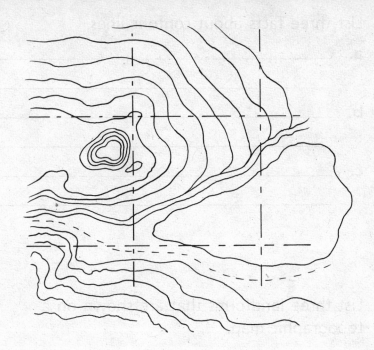

Lombard Street is a very steep street. It has many curves to help cars drive safely.

Mapping Surface Features

There are many kinds of maps. Some maps show a certain part of Earth, such as a city, state, or country.

One special type of map is a **topographic map**. A topographic map shows the shape of land features and their **elevations**, or heights above sea level. **Contour lines** connect points on the map that have the same elevation. The distance between contour lines shows the change in elevation.

Contour lines tell you about the shape and steepness of the land. You can measure the height of a mountain using the contour lines on a map. These lines can also show how deep the ocean is or how steep a slope is.

7. The maps shown here are called topographic maps.

a. Tell what a topographic map does. _____

_____

_____

b. Explain how heights above sea level are shown on a topographic map. _____

_____

_____

c. Darken in one of the contour lines on the map above.

25

8. List three facts about contour lines.

a. _____
_____

b. _____
_____

c. _____
_____

9. List three landforms that are shown on a topographic map.

a. _____

b. _____

c. _____

Contour lines never cross on a map. Contour lines that are very close together show a steep slope. Contour lines that are far apart show that the land is flat.

Topographic maps show rivers, lakes, and different kinds of plants. Special marks also show whether the beach is sandy or rocky. Some maps also show the details below the ocean, such as a coral reef.

CONTRA COSTA COUNTY The many contour lines close together show mountains and valleys east of the bay.

SAN JOSE Flat land borders the south end of the bay. Contour lines are few and far apart.

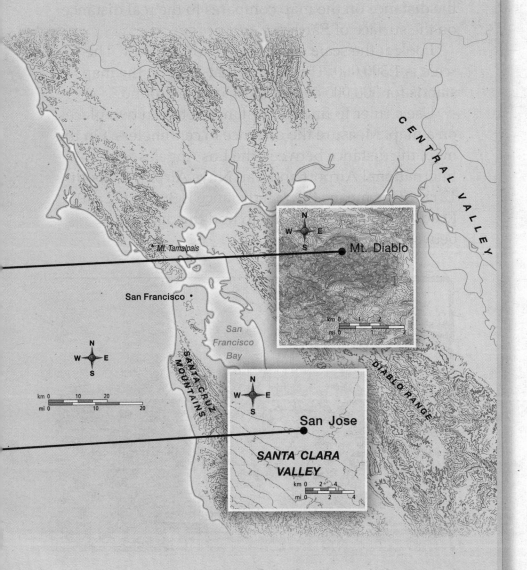

10. Find on the map the areas shown in each photo. What do the contour lines tell you about each area?

a. Mt. Diabolo: _____

_____

_____

b. San Jose: _____

_____

_____

I Wonder . . . Suppose that you and your family are planning a hiking trip. You want to stay away from steep slopes. What would you look for on a topographic map?

_____

_____

_____

_____

_____

_____

_____

27

11. What does a map scale show?

_____

_____

12. (Circle) the city names Los Angeles and Santa Clarita on the map. How could you use the map scale to find the distance between these two cities?

_____

_____

_____

_____

Map Scale

Remember that a map is a model of a real place. A good map must have a scale. A map scale shows how the distance on the map compares to the real distance on the surface of Earth.

Look at the scale on the map shown below. The scale is 1:300,000. This means that 1 cm on the map stands for 300,000 cm, or 3 km, on the ground.

Use a ruler to find the distance between two places on a map. Measure the distance in centimeters. On this map, the distance between the Los Angeles International Airport and Van Nuys Airport is about 12 cm. This means the real distance is 36 km (22 mi). Read a map scale carefully to find the distance between two places.

A map scale is used to find the real distance between two places.

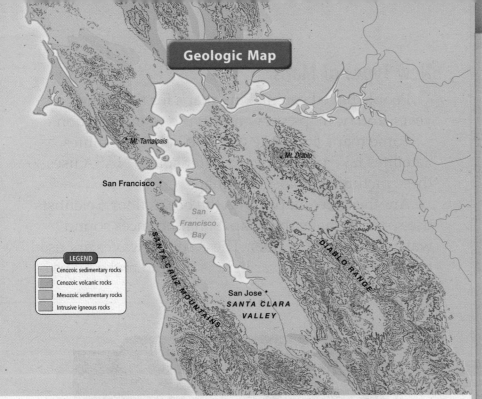

Geologic Map

LEGEND
- Cenozoic sedimentary rocks
- Cenozoic volcanic rocks
- Mesozoic sedimentary rocks
- Intrusive igneous rocks

Mt. Tamalpais

San Francisco

San Francisco Bay

SANTA CRUZ MOUNTAINS

Mt. Diablo

DIABLO RANGE

San Jose
SANTA CLARA VALLEY

This geologic map shows the San Francisco Bay area. Different colors show the different types of surface rocks. Contour lines show the features of the land.

Geologic Maps

Some maps show special kinds of information. A geologic map shows different types of surface rocks. It can also show where rocks are located. Rivers and lakes are sometimes found on a geologic map.

Why do scientists study these maps? Different types of rocks can help scientists find minerals, water, or oil. These maps also help scientists find areas that may be hit by an earthquake or other disaster.

Geologic maps can also help builders. Builders can design safer buildings, roads, and bridges with the help of these maps.

13. What does a geologic map usually show?

_____

_____

_____

14. Use the Venn diagram to compare and contrast topographic and geologic maps.

Comparing Topographic and Geologic Maps

Topographic Maps   Geologic Maps

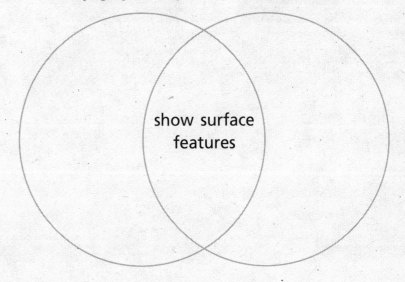

show surface features

15. Fill in the blanks in the table to describe three types of maps made by using new technologies.

Technology	How It Is Used
Satellites	
	used to map the ocean floor
Laser light	

New Types of Maps

People have been making maps for thousands of years. Today, maps show new types of information.

Some maps are made with the help of satellites. Satellites take pictures from outer space. NASA uses these pictures to make new maps.

Another new map shows the ocean floor. Scientists use sonar to make this map. Sonar bounces sound waves off the ocean floor. These sound waves are used to measure depth. Laser light is used to make maps of coral reefs.

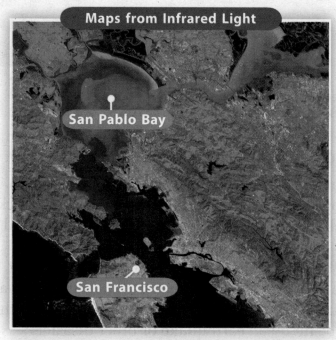

Maps from Infrared Light

San Pablo Bay

San Francisco

NASA satellites use infrared light to take pictures of Earth's surface. The infrared light maps can show different things. The colors in this map show differences in land use.

Maps from Infrared Light

San Pablo Bay

San Francisco

The colors in this infrared light map show differences in water temperature.

Twenty-seven satellites make up the Global Positioning System (GPS). These satellites orbit, or travel around, the planet. Radio signals are sent from GPS satellites to airplanes and cars. GPS measures the distance from the system to at least four satellites. That means GPS is very accurate. This system helps pilots and drivers map their location.

Technology keeps changing and improving. As this happens, the maps people use to understand Earth will get better and better.

16. What is the Global Positioning System (GPS) made up of?

_____

17. What kind of signals does GPS use?

_____

I Wonder . . . People have been making maps for thousands of years. Maps made today are much more accurate than those made long ago. Why do you think this is so?

_____

_____

_____

_____

_____

_____

Summary Earth's surface includes water and land. Surface features can be identified by their location, shape, and elevation. List four surface features.

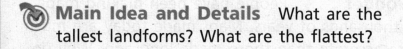

a. _____

b. _____

c. _____

d. _____

Main Idea and Details What are the tallest landforms? What are the flattest?

Tallest: _____

Flattest: _____

This picture of Earth was taken from a satellite.

Humans have put many satellites into orbit around Earth. They do thousands of jobs for us every day. They help us better understand our planet and everything around it in space.

MAIN IDEA AND DETAILS

What are the tallest landforms? What are the flattest?

asthenosphere (as THEN uh sfir) the plastic part of the mantle beneath the lithosphere

astenosfera parte flexible del manto que hay bajo la litosfera

contour lines lines on a topographic map that connect points with the same elevation

curvas de nivel líneas sobre un mapa topográfico que conectan puntos que tienen la misma elevación

San Francisco

core the innermost layer of the Earth, which extends to the center of Earth

núcleo capa interna de la Tierra, que llega hasta el centro de ésta

crust the outermost layer of the Earth

corteza capa más externa de la Tierra

crust

elevation height above sea level

elevación altura sobre el nivel del mar

lithosphere (LITH oh sfir) the rigid shell formed by the upper mantle and the crust

litosfera la capa rígida formada por el manto y la corteza

Circle the words that describe layers of Earth. Which layer is not listed on this page?

_____

Visit www.eduplace.com to play puzzles and word games.

(Circle) the English words and their meanings for all the glossary terms on this page that describe ways that Earth can move.

Glossary

mantle the solid layer just below Earth's crust

    manto capa sólida que hay justo debajo de la corteza terrestre

revolution a complete orbit around an object, such as the Sun

    revolución órbita completa alrededor de un objeto, por ejemplo, el Sol

rotation a complete turn about an axis

    rotación vuelta completa alrededor de un eje

topographic map a map that shows the shape of surface features and their elevations

    mapa topográfico mapa que muestra la configuración de la superficie de un terreno y sus elevaciones

Responding

Think About What You Have Read

Vocabulary

❶ The plastic, soft layer of the mantle is called the _____.

   A) asthenosphere

   B) core

   C) crust

   D) lithosphere

Comprehension

❷ What causes the four seasons on Earth?

❸ How is Earth like a compass?

❹ Why are maps useful tools for studying Earth?

Critical Thinking

❺ Unlike other planets, why can Earth support living things? Include at least three reasons in your answer.

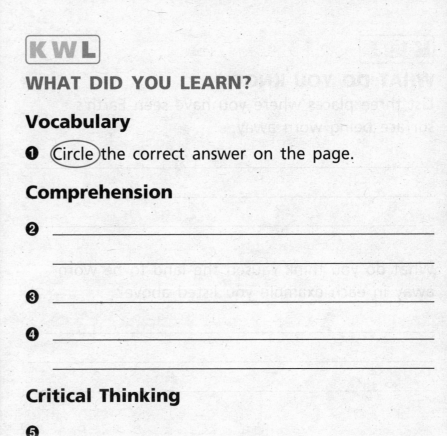

KWL

WHAT DID YOU LEARN?

Vocabulary

❶ Circle the correct answer on the page.

Comprehension

❷ _____

_____

❸ _____

❹ _____

_____

Critical Thinking

❺ _____

_____

_____

_____

_____

Chapter Preview

Shaping Earth's Surface

KWL

WHAT DO YOU KNOW?

List three places where you have seen Earth's surface being worn away.

_____

_____

_____

What do you think caused the land to be worn away in each example you listed above?

_____

_____

_____

Contents

WHAT DO YOU WANT TO KNOW?

Skim the pictures and headings in this chapter. List one thing you want to find out about each topic:

How Earth's surface is worn down _____

_____

_____

How rivers shape the land _____

_____

_____

How beaches are changed _____

_____

_____

VOCABULARY

erosion the carrying away of sediments *(noun)*

sediment small rock pieces produced by weathering *(noun)*

weathering the process by which rock material is broken into smaller pieces *(noun)*

VOCABULARY SKILL: Root Words and Suffixes

Erode is a verb that means "to carry or wear away." When the suffix *-ion*, which means "the act of," is added to *erode*, the word becomes the noun *erosion*. Tell what *erosion* means.

_____

_____

_____

2.a. Students know that water running downhill shapes landscapes, including California's landscapes.
2.d. Students know that natural events change human and wildlife habitats.

1 How Is Earth's Surface Worn Down?

Weathering and erosion wear down Earth's surface features.

Weathering

Earth's crust is mostly solid rock. The rocks are broken into pieces by **weathering**. Weathering is a force that breaks something down. There are two types of weathering: mechanical and chemical.

Mechanical weathering takes place when large rocks break into smaller pieces. Small rock pieces are called sediment.

Moving air and water can cause mechanical weathering. Water trickles into the cracks of rocks. When water freezes, it takes up more space. The frozen water can break a rock apart.

Living things can cause mechanical weathering. Plant roots can grow through a crack and break a rock apart. Animals burrow and push against rocks. They make space for water to move deeper into the rocks and soil.

Trees are strong enough to move or split rocks as they grow.

Chemical weathering is different from mechanical weathering. Chemical weathering can change what the rock is made of.

Water causes chemical weathering. Water can break down some minerals that make up rocks. Water also mixes with air and soil to form weak acids. These acids can break down minerals in some kinds of rocks.

Most weathering takes place at Earth's surface. But water also soaks into the ground. This water can weather rocks below the surface. Water can make a hole in a rock underground. Over time, this hole grows large enough to be called a cave.

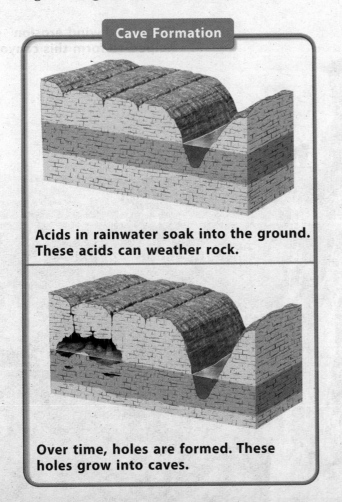

Cave Formation

Acids in rainwater soak into the ground. These acids can weather rock.

Over time, holes are formed. These holes grow into caves.

1. Define mechanical weathering.

   _____

   _____

2. List three causes of mechanical weathering.

   a. _____

   b. _____

   c. _____

3. Tell how water can cause chemical weathering.

Cause	Effect
Water mixes with air and soil to form weak acids.	

39

4. Compare and contrast weathering and erosion.

Comparing Weathering and Erosion

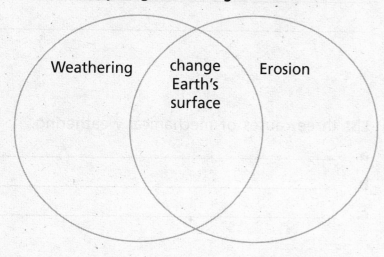

Weathering | change Earth's surface | Erosion

5. List four causes of erosion.

a. _____

b. _____

c. _____

d. _____

Erosion

Weathering breaks down rock into smaller pieces called **sediments**. When sediments are carried away, it is called **erosion** (e ROH zhuhn). Rivers and streams can cause erosion. Wind, ice, and gravity can also cause erosion.

Wind erosion is powerful in deserts and other dry areas. Strong winds pick up small pieces of sediment. The wind and the sediment blow against larger rocks. This action also causes weathering.

Water and wind erosion helped to form this canyon.

40

Have you ever seen sand dunes on a beach? Dunes are caused by wind erosion. The sediment on a beach is mostly sand. The wind picks up sand and then drops it nearby. The falling sand causes other pieces to move. The sand moves together and makes the shape of a dune.

Wind sweeps sand into sand dunes.

6. Complete the diagram to explain how wind erosion helped form the sand dunes on this page.

Strong winds pick up _____.

↓

The wind drops the sand _____.

↓

The falling sand causes _____.

↓

The sand moves together and makes a _____.

I Wonder . . . Suppose that you were able to travel to a planet named Dune. What do you think it would be like there?

_____

_____

_____

_____

41

7. A mountain of frozen water is called a
_____.

8. Circle the word in each sentence that makes the statement about glaciers correct.

a. Glaciers covered much of Earth's surface (hundreds, thousands) of years ago.

b. Glaciers move very (slowly, quickly).

c. As glaciers moved over the surface, they (changed, left unchanged) the ground underneath them.

d. When a glacier melts, it may form (a lake, an ocean).

e. Glaciers carved out (the Great Lakes, the Salton Sea).

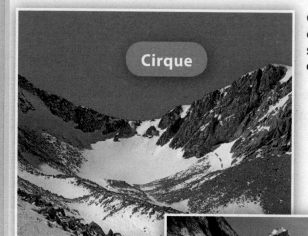

Glaciers carve out bowl-shaped spaces called cirques.

Cirque

When a glacier melts, it becomes a lake.

Frozen water can also change the shape of the land. A glacier is a mountain of frozen water. Thousands of years ago, glaciers covered much of Earth's surface. The ice was so heavy that it pushed and dented the ground underneath it.

Glaciers moved very slowly. They pushed large amounts of soil and rock as they moved. Glaciers helped shape the rolling plains in the northern United States. They also carved out the Great Lakes.

Landslides and Sinkholes

Sometimes erosion takes place very slowly. Other times it happens very fast. A landslide can happen in minutes.

A landslide is when a large area of rocks and sediments falls down a steep slope or hill. Gravity is the main cause of a landslide. Water also helps by loosening the sediments. Sediments that are very wet can easily slide down a hill. A minor earthquake or volcanic eruption can also start a landslide.

A landslide is strong enough to take houses down a hill.

9. Describe what happens in a landslide.

_____

_____

_____

10. List four causes of landslides.

a. _____

b. _____

c. _____

d. _____

Summary Weathering and erosion wear down Earth's surface features. Complete the sentences to summarize these processes.

_____ breaks rocks into small pieces.

Mechanical weathering breaks larger rocks into pieces called _____.

The carrying away of sediments is called

_____.

Sequence How does water from Earth's surface make a cave?

> Acids in _____ soak into the ground.

↓

> These acids weather rock by _____.

↓

> Over time, holes are formed. The holes grow large enough to be called a _____.

Sinkhole **says it all: an area of land sinks into a hole.**

The falling land in a landslide can destroy homes, businesses, and highways. Landslides also destroy plants, trees, and habitats.

You have read about how weathering can make a cave below Earth's surface. After a cave has formed, the rock above it has no support. This rock can fall into the cave below. When this rock falls, a sinkhole is formed.

SEQUENCE

How does water from Earth's surface make a cave?

44

How Do Rivers Shape the Landscape?

2

Water running downhill is a powerful force. Rivers can change the shape of the land.

How Rivers Form

Rivers start high in the mountains. Rain water or melting snow comes together and flows over the land. Gravity pulls the water downhill. Tiny trickles turn into brooks and streams.

Streams join together as they flow downhill. They become a river. Most large rivers are joined by many tributaries. **Tributaries** are streams and small rivers.

Rivers take the shortest and steepest path downhill. All rivers empty into large bodies of water, such as a lake or the ocean.

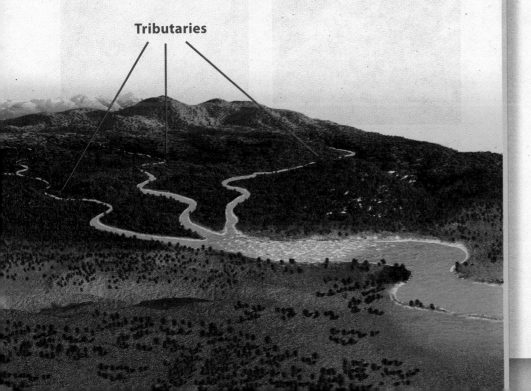

Tributaries

VOCABULARY

alluvial fan fan-shaped deposit of sediment that forms when water flows from a steep slope onto a flat plain *(noun)*

delta a triangle-shaped plain that forms where a river enters the ocean *(noun)*

deposition the process of dropping sediments *(noun)*

meander a bend in a river formed when the river moves across wide, flat regions *(noun)*

tributary a river or a stream feeding into a major river *(noun)*

VOCABULARY SKILL: Root Words and Suffixes

The word *deposition* is made of two parts. The base word *deposit* means "to lay or put down." The suffix *-ion* means "the act of." Use this information to write your own definition of the word *deposition*.

_____

_____

 2.a. Students know that water running downhill shapes landscapes, including California's landscapes.
2.b. Students know that rivers and streams change the land in natural and recurring patterns.

1. Number the events to show the sequence in which rivers form.

_____ Streams join to become a river.

_____ Gravity pulls the water downhill, and tiny trickles turn into streams.

_____ Rivers start high in the mountains.

_____ Rain water or melting snow comes together and flows over land.

_____ Tributaries join the river and it becomes bigger, finally emptying into a larger body of water.

2. Complete these sentences about the changes that rivers make to the area over which they flow.

a. A river _____ the land by breaking down rocks and washing away minerals.

b. A river _____ the land by picking up and moving soil, pebbles, and sediments.

The rushing water of a river weathers and erodes the land. Rock is broken down and minerals are washed away. Soil, pebbles, and sediment are picked up and moved.

A river carves out a wider path over time. The water and rocks erode, or cut deeper into, the riverbed. A river valley forms. Sometimes a river can turn a valley into a canyon.

A mountain stream weathers rocks and carries sediment downstream.

Rivers can cut V-shaped valleys in the land. These valleys are called canyons.

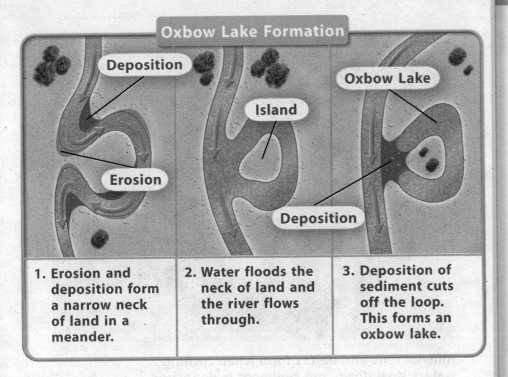

Oxbow Lake Formation

Deposition

Island

Oxbow Lake

Erosion

Deposition

1. Erosion and deposition form a narrow neck of land in a meander.

2. Water floods the neck of land and the river flows through.

3. Deposition of sediment cuts off the loop. This forms an oxbow lake.

Deposition

Rivers carry sediment as they flow to the ocean. Some of the sediment is dropped along the river. The process of dropping sediment is called **deposition** (dep uh ZISH uhn). Deposition builds up the land. It forms many land features.

Meanders and Oxbow Lakes A river that moves across flat land begins to wind around in curves. These curves are called **meanders** (me AN duhrz). The flow of the river changes its speed from the inside to the outside of each curve.

Look at the diagram of the oxbow lake. Sometimes, the curves of a river are so close together that the water breaks through the land. A loop forms in the river. Sediment cuts off the loop and it becomes an oxbow lake.

3. Erosion and deposition are both active in rivers. Compare and contrast erosion and deposition.

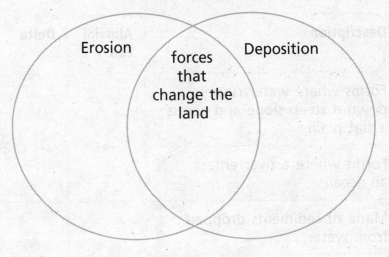

Erosion and Deposition

Erosion

forces that change the land

Deposition

4. Explain how erosion and deposition work together to form an oxbow lake.

_____

_____

_____

_____

5. Read each description. Decide whether it applies to alluvial fans, deltas, or both. Put an X in the box if it applies.

Description	Alluvial Fan	Delta
Forms where water rushes down a steep slope and across a flat plain		
Forms where a river enters an ocean		
Made of sediments dropped from water		

Alluvial fans and deltas form when rushing waters slow down and sediment is deposited.

Alluvial Fans and Deltas Sometimes a change in the flow of a river makes a special kind of landmass. An **alluvial fan** (ah LOO vi uhl fan) is a fan-shaped landmass that forms after water rushes down a steep slope. The water slows down when it comes to a flat plain. This forms the alluvial fan.

A **delta** is a low plain that forms at the place where a river enters the ocean. Sediment is dropped in this area. A large river ends in a large delta.

Floods

Flooding changes Earth's surface. Seasonal changes in rainfall or snowfall cause flooding. Most floods usually happen in the spring.

A very snowy winter or a sudden warm spell causes extra water to enter a river. When this water reaches the lowlands, it spills over the riverbanks.

The Mississippi River delta is called a "bird's foot delta" because of its shape.

6. Put a check next to each statement about flooding that is *true*.

_____ Flooding changes Earth's surface.

_____ Most floods occurs in winter, when snowfall is heaviest.

_____ A very snowy winter followed by a sudden warm spell can cause flooding.

Summary   Water running downhill changes Earth's surface. Rivers erode the land, move sediment, change course, and flood. List two effects of flooding.

a. _____

_____

b. _____

_____

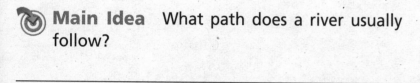 **Main Idea**   What path does a river usually follow?

_____

_____

_____

The Mississippi Flood of 1993 destroyed homes and businesses.

Severe storms also cause floods. A sudden flood after a storm is called a flash flood. Broken dams and levees cause flooding, too. Levees are mounds of dirt built to hold back a river. A broken levee caused the flooding in New Orleans in 2005.

Floods can ruin homes, businesses, and crops. Flooding is especially dangerous in cities. The sewers in cities can overflow. This is a serious health hazard.

MAIN IDEA

What path does a river usually follow?

How Do Beaches Change?

3

Erosion and deposition form beaches. Sand is delivered by rivers. The waves of the ocean move the sand along the coast.

Shaping Shorelines

Wind and water change the shoreline. The waves of the ocean change the shape of the land. Water flows into cracks in rocks. Salt in the water can make a rock break apart.

Land that sticks out into the ocean is eroded first. **Headlands** are narrow sections of land that jut out into the ocean. Waves crash against the bottom of the headlands. Rocks above may fall. This forms steep rock features called **cliffs**.

Weaker rock is worn away more quickly than stronger rock. Holes called **sea caves** are left behind. Sea caves may join to form an **arch**.

As erosion continues, the top of the arch may fall. One side of the arch is left standing alone. This rock column is called a **sea stack**.

VOCABULARY

arch a formation caused in a narrow headland when two sea caves join *(noun)*

barrier island a sandbar that runs parallel to the shore *(noun)*

beach sand or other loose sediment that has been deposited along a shoreline *(noun)*

cliff steep rock feature *(noun)*

headland narrow section of land that juts out into the ocean *(noun)*

sandbar a ridge of sand below the water's surface *(noun)*

sea cave a hole in a headland formed when weaker rock is worn away more quickly than stronger rock *(noun)*

sea stack offshore column of rock created by wave erosion *(noun)*

spit sandbar that rises above the water level and has one end attached to land *(noun)*

2.c. Students know that beaches change.

1. Complete the chart to show how shorelines are shaped.

_____ are narrow sections of land that jut out into the ocean.

_____ crash against the bottom of the headlands. Rocks fall. A _____ forms.

Weaker rock is worn away more _____ than stronger rock. Holes called _____ are left behind. Sea caves may join to form an _____ .

Sometimes the top of the arch falls. One side of the arch is left standing. This column is called a _____ .

52

A **beach** is made up of sand or other loose sediment that has been dropped along a shoreline. Beaches are dynamic systems. This means that they are always changing.

Ocean currents and waves carry sediment. Some currents run parallel to the shore. These currents may form a **sandbar**. A sandbar is a ridge of sand below the water's surface.

Rock sediment is weathered by water to form sand.

sea stack

barrier island

sandbar

beach

A **spit** is a sandbar that rises above the water level and has one end attached to the shore. The end of the spit that is not joined to land is usually shaped like a hook.

A **barrier island** is a sandbar that runs parallel to the shore. Some barrier islands were once spits. Wave erosion can break away land, turning the spit into a barrier island. Storms also form barrier islands. Some barrier islands were sand dunes that flooded.

Barrier islands protect the shoreline from storm damage. They also provide habitats for plants and animals.

Arches form when erosion cuts a hole through a narrow headland.

headland

spit

2. Make a check next to each feature that forms through deposition. Put an X next to each feature that forms through erosion.

_____ barrier island

_____ headlands   _____ beach

_____ spit   _____ sandbar

_____ cliffs   _____ arch

3. Explain how spits and barrier islands are related to sandbars.

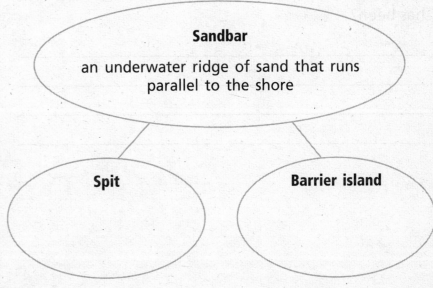

Sandbar

an underwater ridge of sand that runs parallel to the shore

Spit

Barrier island

53

4. What is sand?

_____

_____

5. How does sand form?

_____

_____

I Wonder . . . Your friend John has been on vacation. He was on an island, but he won't tell which one. You see a few grains of black sand fall out of his pocket. Where do you think he has been?

_____

_____

_____

Sand: Up Close

Sand is very small pieces of different rocks and minerals. Sediment dropped by rivers rubs together to form sand. A sand grain can be as small as a grain of salt.

Not all sand is tan. Places with volcanoes have black sand beaches. The sand comes from the sediment of lava and ash from the volcanoes. Some beaches have sand that is from coral reefs.

When you look closely at grains of sand, you will see that they are different sizes, shapes, and colors.

Black sand is common on Hawaii and other volcanic islands.

On California beaches, parts of shells are mixed in the sand.

Rivers may deposit silt along their shores to form thin, narrow beaches.

Changes in Sea Level

The sea level can change because of tides. This change also shapes the shoreline. Tides are caused by the Moon's gravitational pull on Earth. At high tide, the water level is higher along the shoreline. At low tide, the water lever is lower and the beach is wider.

High tide and low tide can be different from place to place. The shape of the shoreline and the ocean floor affect the tide height. Tides cause currents to move sediment from one place to another.

The sea level has risen and fallen many times during Earth's history. What caused these changes? The main reason was Earth's temperature. When it got warmer on Earth, glaciers melted and the ocean levels went up.

Tides cause parts of the shoreline to be covered with water for a part of each day.

6. Define *tides*, and tell what causes them.

_____

_____

7. Look at the pictures on this page. Decide which picture shows high tide and which picture shows low tide. Label the pictures.

8. The shape of the _____ and the shape of the _____ can affect the height of tides in an area.

9. What has caused sea level changes during Earth's history?

_____

_____

_____

55

10. Complete the table to explain how different factors affect beaches.

Factor	How It Affects Beaches
	Carried into the ocean and washes up on beaches
Oil	
Building Construction	

11. Tell the name of the state agency that works to protect beaches in California.

_____

56

Beach Issues

Beach pollution is a problem in every coastal state in the United States today. Polluted rivers and streams carry water into the ocean. This polluted water washes up onto beaches. After a heavy storm, overflowing sewers may dump waste into rivers.

Oil can destroy a beach quickly. Oil wells or oil tankers sometimes spill oil into the ocean. If the oil reaches the beach, it can hurt the ecosystem. Animals, plants, rocks, and sand all become coated in oil. It is very hard to clean the beach and remove all the oil.

Oil that is spilled at sea washes onto the beach. Cleaning up oil spills is very hard to do.

Beach sand can be made of different types of rocks, minerals, plants, and shells.

Building houses along the beach can also be a problem. Construction can change the shape of a beach and destroy salt marshes. It can also damage plant and animal life.

The state government works to protect beaches. The California Coastal Commission is in charge of protecting this special land feature. Beaches are the meeting place of Earth's land, air, and oceans. Keeping beaches clean is an important goal for everyone.

COMPARE AND CONTRAST

What are some different types of beach sand?

Summary Beach features are formed through erosion and deposition. Changes in sea level also shape shorelines. What are two causes of sea-level changes?

a. _____

_____

b. _____

_____

Compare and Contrast What are three different types of beach sand?

a. _____

b. _____

c. _____

List two or more of the terms on these pages and explain why they could be grouped together.

_____

_____

_____

_____

alluvial fan (ah LOO vi uhl fan) fan-shaped deposit of sediment that forms when water flows from a steep slope onto a flat plain

abanico fluvial depósito de sedimento en forma de abanico que aparece cuando el agua fluye por una pendiente hacia una llanura

arch a formation caused in a narrow headland when two sea caves join

arco formación que se produce en un cabo cuando dos cuevas marinas se unen

barrier island a sandbar that runs parallel to the shore

arrecife barrera de arena que corre paralela a la costa

beach sand or other loose sediment that has been deposited along a shoreline

playa arena u otro sedimento suelto que se ha depositado a lo largo de la costa

cliff steep rock feature

acantilado roca muy escarpada

Glossary

delta a triangle-shaped plain that forms where a river enters the ocean

delta llanura baja de forma triangular que se forma cuando un río llega al océano

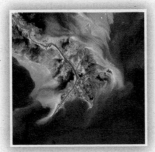

deposition (dep uh ZISH uhn) the process of dropping sediments

sedimentación proceso por el cual se depositan sedimentos

erosion (e ROH zhuhn) the carrying away of sediments

erosión desplazamiento de sedimentos

headland narrow section of land that juts out into the ocean

cabo parte estrecha de tierra que penetra en el océano

meander (me AN duhr) a bend in a river formed when the river moves across wide, flat regions

meandros curvatura de un río que se forma cuando este se mueve por superficies anchas y llanas

sandbar a ridge of sand below the water's surface

banco de arena cresta de arena bajo la superficie del agua

Read the definitions of *erosion* and *deposition*. Fill in the diagram to show how these words are related.

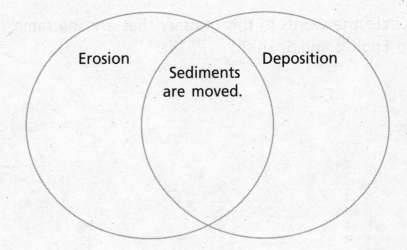

Erosion

Sediments are moved.

Deposition

Visit www.eduplace.com to play puzzles and word games.

Circle the words in this glossary that are the same in English and Spanish.

Glossary

sea cave a hole in a headland formed when weaker rock is worn away more quickly than stronger rock

cueva marina agujero que se forma en un cabo cuando las rocas débiles se desgastan antes que las fuertes

sea stack offshore column of rock created by wave erosion

islote columna de roca cerca de la costa creada por erosión producida por las olas

sediment small rock pieces produced by weathering

sedimento trozos pequeños de roca producidos por desgaste

spit sandbar that rises above the water level and has one end attached to land

punta banco de arena que surge del mar y uno de sus extremos está unido a la costa

tributary a river or a stream feeding into a major river

tributario río o corriente que desemboca en un río mayor

weathering the process by which rock material is broken into smaller pieces

meteorización el proceso por el cual el material rocoso se rompe en pedazos más pequeños

Think About What You Have Read

Vocabulary

❶ The act of building up land is _____.

   A) deposition

   B) erosion

   C) sediment

   D) weathering

Comprehension

❷ Describe how erosion wears down Earth's surface.

❸ What causes seasonal flooding?

❹ How does pollution on beaches compare to pollution in other places?

Critical Thinking

❺ What solutions would you suggest to a town that has a lot of damage because of seasonal flooding?

WHAT DID YOU LEARN?

Vocabulary

❶ Circle the correct answer on the page.

Comprehension

❷ _____

   _____

   _____

❸ _____

   _____

❹ _____

   _____

Critical Thinking

❺ _____

   _____

WHAT DO YOU KNOW?

What happens during an earthquake?

_____

_____

_____

How do mountains form?

_____

_____

_____

Evidence of Plate Tectonics

Contents

WHAT DO YOU WANT TO KNOW?
Skim the pictures and headings in this chapter. List one thing you want to find out about Earth's past by learning about these topics:

Fossils _____

_____

_____

Earth's surface _____

_____

_____

Tectonic plates _____

_____

_____

Plate boundaries _____

_____

_____

Lesson Preview

VOCABULARY

fossil the preserved remains or traces of an organism that lived in the distant past *(noun)*

strata horizontal layers of rock *(noun)*

VOCABULARY SKILL: Word Content

In this lesson, you will learn about an ancient continent called *Pangaea*. *Pangaea* comes from two Greek words. *Pan* means "all," and *gaea* means "land." Put these two Greek words together, and then write what you think Pangaea looked like.

_____

_____

_____

_____

_____

1 What Do Rocks and Fossils Reveal?

Earth's rock layers and fossils can be used to explain Earth's history.

Evidence of Change

Rocks are always changing from one form to another. They change through weathering, erosion, heating, and cooling.

Glaciers are thick sheets of ice that move slowly across the land. Glaciers cause change in the surface of the land. They grind rocks and sculpt the land as they move. During the ice ages, glaciers once covered large land areas.

Scientists study rocks to figure out events in Earth's history. The information in rocks is called the rock record.

The Rocky Mountains have sharp peaks. These peaks show that not much erosion has occurred.

The Appalachian Mountains have rounded peaks. Rounded peaks are evidence of erosion.

1.a. Students know that there is evidence of plate tectonics.

The Rock Record

Sediment is always found in layers, or **strata**. The layers at the bottom are usually the oldest. The location of a layer in the rock tells the age of the sediment that formed it.

Each layer of rock has specific properties, such as minerals or chemicals. Other properties are color, texture, and thickness.

Horizontal layers of rock are called strata.

1. List four things that cause rocks to change.

   a. _____

   b. _____

   c. _____

   d. _____

2. Complete the diagram to tell what properties strata may have.

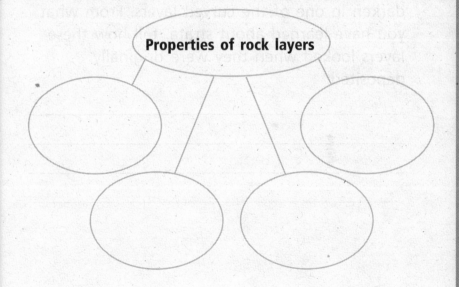

Properties of rock layers

3. List two things that surprised scientists studying rock layers in the early 1900s.

a. _____

_____

b. _____

_____

4. Look at the photo on this page. Find some curved strata in the rock. Use your pencil to darken in one of the curved layers. From what you have learned about strata, tell how these layers looked when they were originally deposited.

_____

_____

_____

In the early 1900s, scientists made maps of rock layers with details about each layer. They were surprised to find the remains of fish and animals with shells in the middle of mountains. The scientists did not know how fish and shells could be deposited so far above sea level.

Some of the strata was curved and folded. This was another mystery that scientists wanted to study.

Scientists ask questions to make sense of the things they study.

The Fossil Record

A **fossil** is the preserved remains of an organism that lived in the distant past. Fossils are found in layers of sediment. Studying fossils can tell us about Earth's history.

How Fossils Form Fossils come from an animal's bones, shells, and other hard parts. These parts are not easily broken down or eaten.

A fossil can form when an animal or a shell is buried in the ground. The soft parts of an animal decay. Over many years, minerals in the water soak into the bones of the animal or into a shell. These minerals preserve the shape and size of the bone or shell. The organism becomes a fossil.

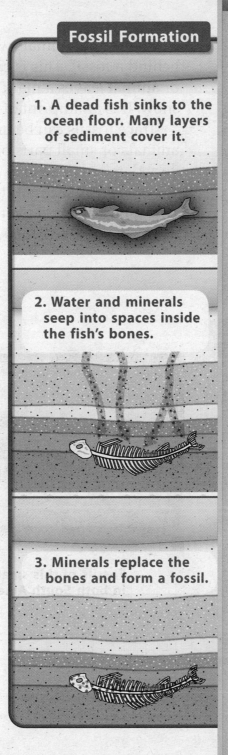

Fossil Formation

1. **A dead fish sinks to the ocean floor. Many layers of sediment cover it.**

2. **Water and minerals seep into spaces inside the fish's bones.**

3. **Minerals replace the bones and form a fossil.**

5. Complete the diagram to explain how a fossil fish forms.

A dead fish sinks to the ocean floor. Many _____ cover it.

Water and _____ seep into the spaces inside the fish's bones.

_____ replace the bones and form a _____.

6. Tell how a plant or animal without hard parts can be preserved as a fossil.

_____

_____

_____

I Wonder . . . Suppose that you find a fossil of an unknown animal in the same layer as a fossil clam. What might you conclude about where the unknown animal lived?

_____

_____

_____

_____

_____

Plants and animals without hard parts can leave behind a fossil. This is called a trace fossil. The plant or animal leaves a mark behind, like a footprint in the snow. It is an imprint of the plant or animal.

Trace fossils can be imprints of whole plants or animals or small parts of them. They often look like very detailed drawings.

Scientists use fossils to learn more about Earth and how it has changed over time. Look at these pictures. What do you think they tell scientists about our planet?

Fossils of this small reptile have been found in both South America and Africa.

Relative Dating Scientists can tell the age of a fossil. They look at the strata of sedimentary rock where the fossil was found. The oldest layer is on the bottom. The most recent is on top. Scientists conclude that the fossil is about as old as the rock around it.

This fossil of a tropical fern was found in a cold climate. This tells us the area was once much warmer.

This fossil of a fish came from a mountain in Wyoming. This shows that the land was once under water.

7. Look at the diagram below.

   a. Where is the oldest layer found? Label it "oldest."

   b. Where is the youngest layer found? Label it "youngest."

8. Describe how scientists can tell the age of a fossil.

   _____

   _____

   _____

9. Why do scientists study fossils?

_____

_____

10. Explain what each fossil find might tell scientists about the past.

Fossil Find	What It Tells Scientists
Tropical fern fossil	
Fish fossil found far away from water	

I Wonder . . . Will scientists in the future find fossils of today's organisms? What do you think?

_____

_____

_____

_____

Clues About the Past Some fossils provide clues about the place where the plants or animals once lived. A fossil of a tropical fern tells that the weather was once warm and humid. Fossils of fish found far away from water tell that the area was once very different. In Earth's past there were shallow seas over some areas that are now land.

Sometimes, fossils of the same plant and animal species have been found on different continents. How could this be explained?

Studying fossils can give us clues about the past.

Continental Drift

You have read that sometimes fish fossils are found far away from water. A meteorologist named Alfred Wegener tried to explain how this could happen.

Wegener's Hypothesis Wegener came up with a hypothesis, a guess based on facts. He said that the continents on Earth moved slowly. This idea was called continental drift.

Wegener had proof to back up his guess. He pointed out that the coast of South America and western Africa seemed to fit together like puzzle pieces. Fossils of the same plants and animals were found in both areas.

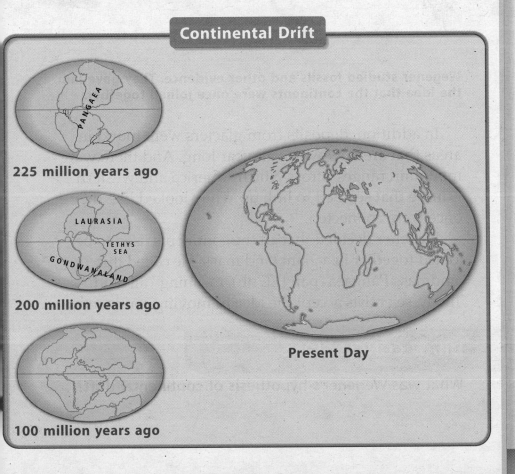

Continental Drift

225 million years ago

200 million years ago

Present Day

100 million years ago

11. Who was Alfred Wegener, and what was his hypothesis?

_____

_____

_____

_____

_____

_____

12. List two forms of proof Wegener used to back up his hypothesis.

a. _____

_____

_____

b. _____

_____

_____

71

Summary   Earth's rocks layers and fossils contain evidence that can be used to explain Earth's history. List two things that scientists can learn by studying fossils.

a. _____

b. _____

 Draw Conclusions   What was Wegener's hypothesis of continental drift?

Data: Glacial deposits found in areas that are now warm all year long	Data: South American and African coasts seem to fit together; similar fossils found on both continents	Data: Mountain ranges in North America and Europe that seem to link up

Conclusion

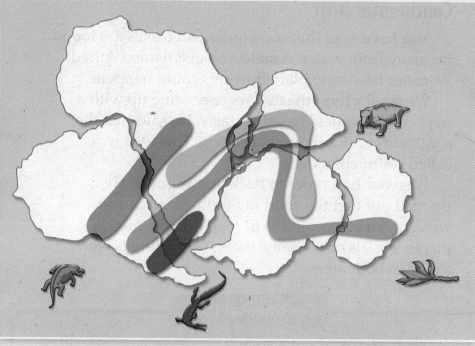

Wegener studied fossils and other evidence. They gave him the idea that the continents were once joined together.

In addition, deposits from glaciers were found in areas that are now warm all year long. And there were mountain ranges across North America and western Europe that seemed to link up. They looked like they once were connected.

Wegener decided that all the continents used to be joined together in a giant land mass. He called this landmass Pangaea (pan JEE uh), meaning "all land." Today, scientists accept the idea of moving continents.

DRAW CONCLUSIONS

What was Wegener's hypothesis of continental drift?

What Are Tectonic Plates?

Earth's outside layer is made up of large, moving plates. Earthquakes, volcanoes, and mid-ocean ridges are proof of these plates.

Continents and Tectonic Plates

In the 1960s, scientists came up with a new theory, or idea. This theory is called plate tectonics (tek THAN iks). Tectonics is the word for the movements that change Earth's crust.

The continents are part of Earth's crust. The crust and the upper mantle form the lithosphere. The lithosphere is broken into huge parts called **tectonic plates**. These tectonic plates move. The continents ride along on top, like cargo on a ship.

The Himalaya Mountains formed when the Indian Plate and the Eurasian plate crashed into each other.

VOCABULARY

fault a crack in Earth's crust along which movement takes place *(noun)*

magma hot melted rock below Earth's surface *(noun)*

plate boundary the edge of a tectonic plate *(noun)*

sea-floor spreading a process in which magma wells up and fills the space between spreading tectonic plates *(noun)*

tectonic plate a giant slab of lithosphere that floats on Earth's mantle *(noun)*

VOCABULARY SKILL: Multiple Meaning Words

The word *fault* has more than one meaning. In science, a fault is a crack in Earth's crust. Think about another meaning for this word. Write a sentence in which you use this other meaning of the word *fault*.

_____

_____

1.a. Students know that there is evidence of plate tectonics.

73

1. What does the word *tectonics* mean?

_____

_____

2. Think back to what you know about the layers of Earth. What word is used to describe the crust and upper mantle?

_____

3. Tectonic plates move in different ways. Tell what happens when plates move in the way described.

Plate Movement	What Happens
Plates crash together.	
Plates grind past each other.	
Plates pull apart.	

Evidence of Moving Plates There is proof of moving plates in places where plates come together, pull apart, or slide past each other.

Mountains form when plates crash together. Pressure causes plates to buckle and fold. When these huge plates fold, a mountain rises up.

A **fault** is a crack in Earth's crust. Plates grind past each other. Pressure builds up. When rocks break and shift there can be an earthquake.

Sometimes plates pull apart. This forms a rift valley. A rift valley is a long, narrow valley.

Sliding plates can break a structure that is built on top of them.

The Rift Valley in Africa is filled in by the Red Sea.

Sea-Floor Spreading

Scientists have made maps of the ocean floor. They discovered a mountain chain underwater. It is called a mid-ocean ridge.

A ridge marks an area where plates move apart. There are ridges in all of Earth's oceans and they all connect. One ridge in the Atlantic Ocean is called the Mid-Atlantic Ridge. It is shaped like the coasts of South America and Africa. This shows that these two continents were once connected. They broke apart along this ridge.

There is a deep valley in the center of a ridge. This valley is called a rift valley.

Magma is melted rock below Earth's surface. When plates spread apart, magma flows up and fills the space in a process called **sea-floor spreading**.

The Mid-Atlantic Ridge runs down the center of the Atlantic Ocean floor.

4. Find the Mid-Atlantic Ridge in the picture. Trace it with your finger.
   a. Tell what happened in the past along this ridge.

   _____

   _____

   _____

   _____

   _____

   b. Tell what is happening now along this ridge. Use the words *sea-floor spreading* and *magma* in your answer.

   _____

   _____

   _____

   _____

   _____

   _____

5. Fill in the diagram to explain how plates can move apart without Earth's getting bigger.

As one plate grows, another shrinks.

Plates grow when
_____
_____
_____
_____

Plates shrink when
_____
_____
_____
_____

Sea-floor spreading helps prove plate tectonics. It explains how plates grow and shrink. Plates grow when they move apart and magma rises up. The magma cools and turns into rock. This rock makes the plates larger.

Plates shrink when one plate moves under another. The sinking plate falls into the mantle of Earth and melts. It will be recycled later as magma.

If plates are growing and shrinking, why does Earth stay the same size? As one plate grows, another shrinks. This way the size of the planet never changes.

As you can see on this map, each continent lies mainly on one plate. As the plates move, so do the continents.

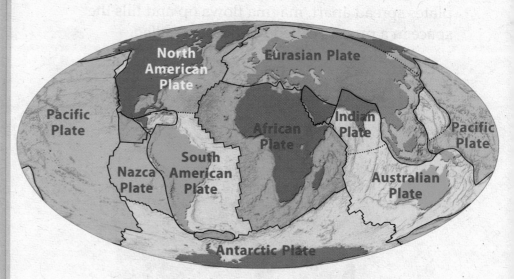

The movement of plates under the ocean floor causes sea-floor spreading.

Earth is like a big magnet with a north pole and a south pole. The magma that flows out of the mid-ocean ridge is rich in iron.

Iron acts like a compass needle. The iron in magma lines up in the direction of Earth's magnetic field. The magma cools and hardens. The new rock has bands that show the record of Earth's magnetic field.

Earth's magnetic field changes from time to time. The iron in rock shows scientists when the rock was formed. The shape of the bands shows that plates are moving.

Matching bands of iron show that the sea floor is spreading. New rock moves outward from the mid-ocean ridge.

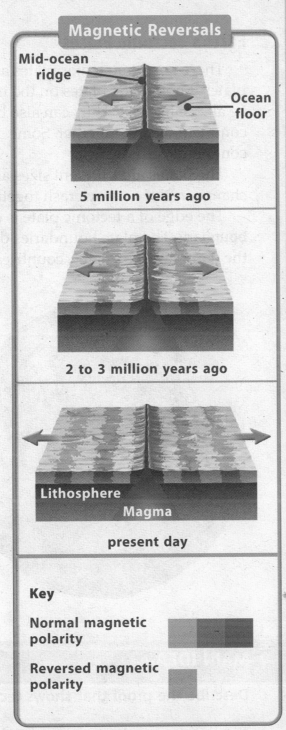

Magnetic Reversals

Mid-ocean ridge

Ocean floor

5 million years ago

2 to 3 million years ago

Lithosphere

Magma

present day

Key

Normal magnetic polarity

Reversed magnetic polarity

6. Complete the diagram to explain how bands of rock in the ocean floor give evidence for sea-floor spreading.

Magma that flows out of the mid-ocean ridge is _____.

The _____ in the magma acts like a compass needle. It lines up _____ _____.

The magma cools and hardens. The band of newly formed rock has _____ _____.

When Earth's magnetic field reverses, the iron of new magma lines up in the opposite way. Parallel bands of rock with matching magnetic records on both sides of the mid-ocean ridge show that the plates are moving apart.

77

Summary Earth's lithosphere is divided into large, moving plates. What is the edge of one of these tectonic plates called?

 Main Idea Describe the proof that shows tectonic plates move.

```
            ┌─────────────────┐
            │ Proof for movement │
            │ of tectonic plates │
            └─────────────────┘
              /              \
        ┌────────┐      ┌────────┐
        │        │      │        │
        └────────┘      └────────┘
```

Earth's Tectonic Plates

There are seven major plates and many smaller plates. Look at the plates on the map. Major plates can be all ocean crust. They can also be ocean crust and continental crust together. Some small plates are continental crust only.

The plates are different sizes and shapes. They can change in size as they crash together and pull apart.

The edge of a tectonic plate is called a **plate boundary**. The plate boundaries do not line up with the boundaries of states, countries, or continents.

MAJOR TECTONIC PLATES This map shows Earth's major tectonic plates. Plates come together along their boundaries.

MAIN IDEA

Describe the proof that shows tectonic plates move.

78

How Do Tectonic Plates Move?

Heat from inside Earth causes currents of movement. These currents move tectonic plates a few centimeters per year.

Oceans and Continents

Earth's crust is different in different places. Continental crust is found under land. It is made of rock that contains lightweight minerals.

Oceanic crust is under the ocean. Oceanic crust is made of rocks formed from magma. They are heavier than the rocks in the continental crust.

The continental crust is much thicker than oceanic crust. Continental crust is about 40 km thick. Oceanic crust is about 7 km thick.

Earth's oceans cover a rocky floor.

VOCABULARY

convection the transfer of thermal energy by the mass movement of particles in a liquid or gas *(noun)*

convection current a current caused by convection that drives fluid through a circular path *(noun)*

VOCABULARY SKILL: Multiple-Meaning Words

A *current* is a smooth forward motion of something. There are different kinds of current. In this lesson, you'll study convection currents. These currents transfer heat. There are also river currents and electric currents. List at least two other types of currents you have heard or studied about.

_____

_____

 1.c. Students know that large tectonic plates slowly move as material in the mantle below them moves.
4.c. Students know that convection brings heat from deep within Earth to the surface.

1. Read each clue. Decide whether it applies to continental or oceanic crust or both. Make an X in the correct box.

Description	Continental Crust	Oceanic Crust
Found under land		
Found under the oceans		
Made of rock with heavy minerals		
Made of rock with lightweight minerals		
About 40 km thick		
About 7 km thick		
Floats on the asthenosphere		

Floating Plates

As you have learned, Earth's crust and the upper mantle form the lithosphere. The lithosphere is broken into parts called tectonic plates. The mantle underneath is hot and plastic-like. This part of the mantle is called the asthenosphere (as THEN uh sfihr).

Why doesn't the lithosphere sink into the layer below it? The reason is that the rocks in the asthenosphere are heavier than the rocks above them.

Earth's tectonic plates are always moving. They slam into each other, slide over or under each other, and grow larger or smaller.

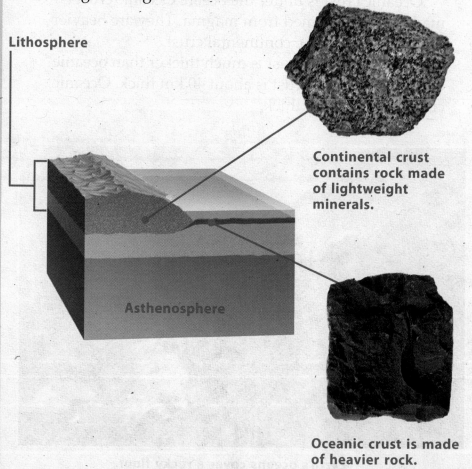

Continental crust contains rock made of lightweight minerals.

Oceanic crust is made of heavier rock.

80

Plate Motion

The inside of Earth is much hotter than its surface. This temperature difference causes a convection current to form in the asthenosphere.

Convection (kahn VEHK shuhn) is the transfer of thermal energy by the mass movement in a fluid, such as air, water, or molten rock. In a **convection current**, convection drives the fluid through a circular path.

Rock is heated deep in the asthenosphere. It spreads out and rises up. Later, it cools and sinks down again. This movement forms the convection current. The current brings energy from Earth's hot center to its surface. These currents can move tectonic plates.

One theory says that convection currents in Earth's mantle move tectonic plates.

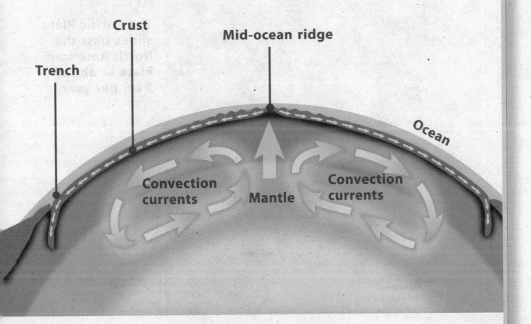

Trench
Crust
Mid-ocean ridge
Convection currents
Mantle
Convection currents
Ocean

2. Find a convection current in the diagram on this page. Trace the current with your finger. Describe the path these currents follow.

_____

3. Number the statements to show the sequence of the movement of a convection current in the asthenosphere.

_____ Rock cools and sinks.

_____ Rock is heated deep in the asthenosphere.

_____ Heated rock spreads out and rises up.

4. Besides moving plates, what else do convection currents do?

_____

_____

5. List three changes in Earth's surface caused by moving plates.

a. _____

b. _____

c. _____

6. What is the best type of technology for measuring the location and movement of tectonic plates?

_____

_____

I Wonder . . .   Oceanic and continental plates often collide. Given what you know about their properties, which plate will be pushed under and which will remain on top? What do you think?

_____

_____

_____

_____

Slow Motion

Tectonic plates move very slowly. It took millions of years for the supercontinent Pangaea to break apart and move.

Tectonic plates move at about the same rate that your fingernails grow. But this slow movement can add up over time. Mountain building, earthquakes, and volcanoes are all caused by these slow-moving plates.

Earth needs tectonic activity. The forces of weathering and erosion would flatten all of Earth's landforms without mountain building. How do you think flat continents would affect life of Earth?

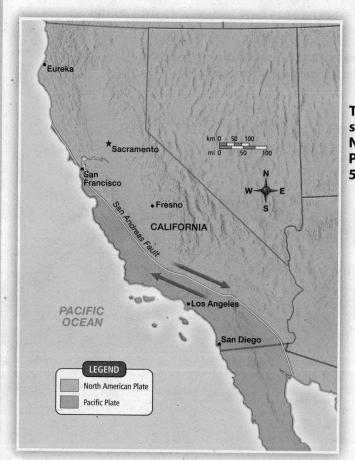

The Pacific Plate slides past the North American Plate at about 5 cm per year.

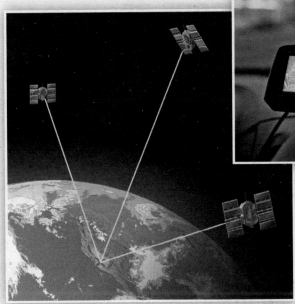

Scientists use GPS signals to measure the movement of tectonic plates.

Measuring Plate Movement

Deep oceans cover some tectonic plates. Other plates are made of large landmasses. Scientists observe Earth from the sky to find out how fast these plates are moving.

The best type of technology for measuring location is the Global Positioning System (GPS). Scientists use GPS to measure certain places over time.

Ground-based radar and laser technology are also used to measure plate movements. Using these tools, scientists can find the rate at which tectonic plates are moving.

DRAW CONCLUSIONS

Why don't continents sink into the asthenosphere?

Summary Heat from Earth's interior drives convection currents in the mantle. These currents move tectonic plates.

About how fast do tectonic plates move?

_____

Draw Conclusions Why don't continents sink into the asthenosphere?

Data:	Data:
_____	_____
_____	_____
_____	_____
_____	

Conclusion: The continents don't sink into the asthenosphere but float upon it.

Lesson Preview

VOCABULARY

subduction a geologic process in which one tectonic plate sinks beneath another *(noun)*

VOCABULARY SKILL: Word Parts

Sometimes breaking a word into parts can help you understand its meaning. In the word *subduction*, the prefix *sub-* mean "under" or "beneath." *Duct* comes from the Latin word *ductus*, which means "to lead." The suffix *-tion* means "the act of." Put these word parts together to write your own definition of the word *subduction*, and then relate it to the definition above.

_____

_____

_____

 1.e. Students know that major geologic events result from plate motions.
1.f. Students can explain major features of California geology in terms of plate tectonics.

4 What Happens at Plate Boundaries?

Movement along plate boundaries causes earthquakes, volcanic eruptions, and mountain building.

Plate Interactions

The movement of tectonic plates can hardly be felt. But at times, it can cause sudden and unexpected changes to Earth's surface.

Some areas of the world have volcanic eruptions and earthquakes while other areas do not. This is because of the boundaries of Earth's tectonic plates. Earthquakes, volcanoes, and other geologic events take place where tectonic plates meet.

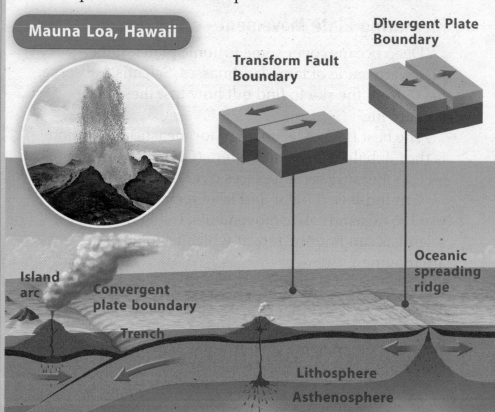

Mauna Loa, Hawaii

Transform Fault Boundary

Divergent Plate Boundary

Island arc

Convergent plate boundary

Trench

Oceanic spreading ridge

Lithosphere

Asthenosphere

Hot spot

Types of Plate Boundaries

There are three types of plate boundaries. They are called convergent, divergent, and transform fault. Each type causes different events and landforms.

Two plates move toward each other at converging boundaries. They crash together and one plate may go up over the other. The upper plate forces the edge of the lower plate under the surface. This process is called **subduction** (suhb DUCK shuhn).

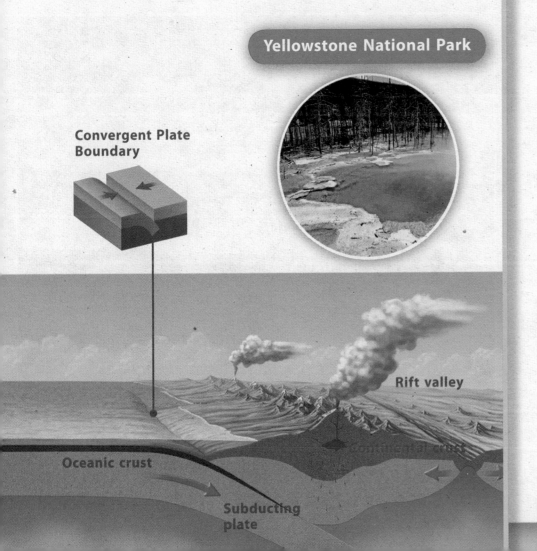

Yellowstone National Park

Convergent Plate Boundary

Oceanic crust

Continental crust

Rift valley

Subducting plate

1. List the three types of plate boundaries.

   a. _____

   b. _____

   c. _____

2. Find a convergent plate boundary on the diagram. Circle the block diagram that shows how the plates are moving at this boundary. Tell what may happen at a convergent boundary.

   _____

   _____

   _____

3. What is subduction?

   _____

   _____

85

4. Complete the diagram summarizing what happens at divergent boundaries.

> Two plates _____ .

↓

> Molten rock _____ .

↓

> The molten rock cools and forms _____ .

5. Describe what happens at transform fault boundaries.

_____

_____

At diverging boundaries, two plates move away from each other. Molten rock rises up between the plates. This rock cools and forms new crust. Diverging boundaries are usually along mid-ocean ridges. As you have learned, when plates move apart along mid-ocean ridges it is called sea-floor spreading.

Plates slide past each other horizontally at transform fault boundaries. Crust buckles and is deformed. It changes shape.

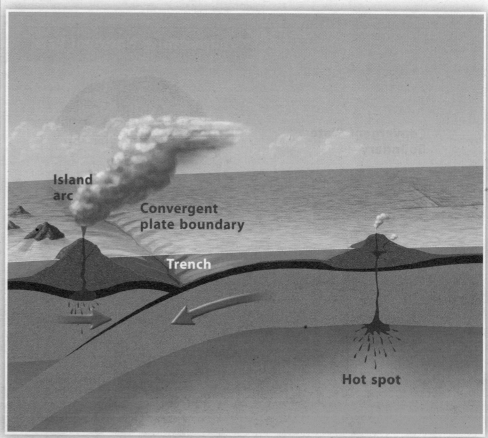

The process of subduction takes place at convergent boundaries.

The Andes formed at a convergent boundary.

Convergent Boundaries Convergent boundaries form where two plates push together. There are three types of convergent boundaries.

At continental-continental boundaries, two plates made of continental crust crash together. The land is pushed up and a high mountain is formed.

At oceanic-continental boundaries, an oceanic plate crashes into a continental plate. The oceanic plate is subducted below the continental plate. This means the oceanic plate goes under the continental plate. A deep, narrow valley called a trench is formed.

At oceanic-oceanic boundaries, two oceanic plates crash together. The cooler, heavier plate sinks below the other one. This type of boundary also forms a trench.

6. Convergent boundaries form where two plates push together. Describe the three types of convergent boundaries. Tell what forms from each interaction.

a. Continental-continental boundaries: _____

_____

_____

_____

What forms: _____

b. Oceanic-continental boundaries: _____

_____

_____

_____

What forms: _____

c. Oceanic-oceanic boundaries: _____

_____

_____

_____

What forms: _____

87

7. Where do divergent boundaries form?

_____

_____

8. Describe a divergent boundary that occurs on land.

_____

_____

_____

_____

9. Describe a divergent boundary that occurs under the ocean.

_____

_____

_____

_____

DIVERGENT BOUNDARY Iceland sits on top of a divergent boundary.

Divergent Boundaries Divergent boundaries form where plates move apart. This usually takes place between two oceanic plates along the mid-ocean ridges.

Some divergent boundaries are on land. Over time, water may fill in the gap between the plates that have moved apart. Volcanic activity and hot springs can also occur at these boundaries.

At an oceanic divergent boundary, magma rises through the crack. It cools and creates new crust. The action forms underwater mountains. Volcanoes and earthquakes also are active along underwater ridges.

TRANSFORM FAULT BOUNDARY The San Andreas Fault zone is a transform fault boundary.

Transform Fault Boundaries Transform fault boundaries form where two plates slide horizontally past each other. A fault is a crack in Earth's crust. It is caused by sliding plates.

Most transform fault boundaries are between oceanic plates. But some transform boundaries can be on land. The San Andreas Fault is a well-known fault that runs along the west coast of California. Earthquakes are common when pressure between the two plates builds up and then is suddenly released.

10. Tell what happens at a transform fault boundary.

_____

_____

_____

_____

I Wonder . . . Would California have as many earthquakes if the San Andreas Fault did not run through the state? What do you think?

_____

_____

_____

_____

11. Trace the Ring of Fire on the diagram. Put a check next to the statements that are *true* about the Ring of Fire.

___ The Ring of Fire borders the Pacific Ocean.

___ All earthquake and volcanic activity on Earth takes place along the Ring of Fire.

___ The Pacific Plate converges with many continental plates along the Ring of fire.

___ California is located along the Ring of Fire.

___ The pattern of earthquakes and volcanoes around the Ring of Fire is more proof of plate tectonics.

I Wonder . . . Why is there no Ring of Fire around the edges of the Atlantic Ocean? What do you think?

_____

_____

_____

_____

90

Ring of Fire

New Zealand

Hawaii

The Ring of Fire

Many earthquakes and volcanoes take place on land that borders the Pacific Ocean. This area is called the Ring of Fire. You can see this area on the map above.

The Pacific Plate converges with many continental plates along the Ring of Fire. Faulting between the Pacific Plate and the continental plates leads to earthquake and volcanic activity.

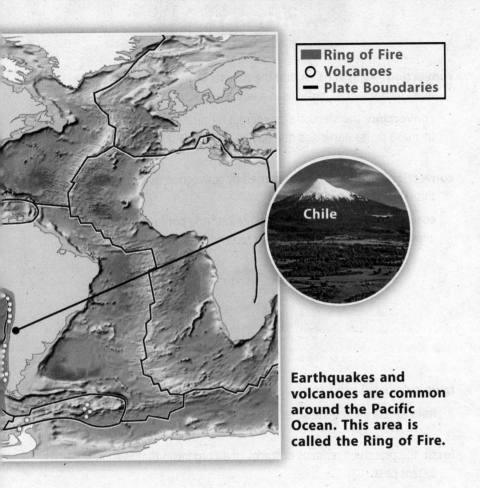

Ring of Fire
○ Volcanoes
— Plate Boundaries

Chile

Earthquakes and volcanoes are common around the Pacific Ocean. This area is called the Ring of Fire.

Not all earthquake and volcanic activity takes place along the Ring of Fire. Diverging plates can also cause earthquakes and volcanoes.

The pattern of earthquakes and volcanoes along plate boundaries is more proof of plate tectonics.

CAUSE AND EFFECT

What causes faults in Earth's crust?

Summary Movement along plate boundaries causes geologic events such as earthquakes, volcanic eruptions, and mountain building. Look at each diagram. Label the type of plate boundary shown.

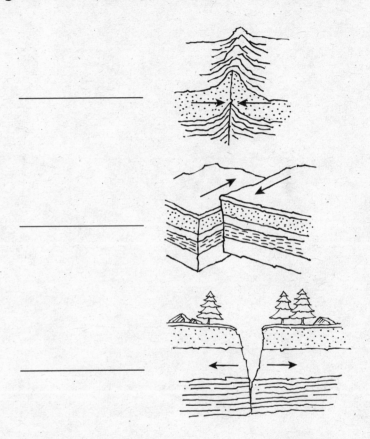

_____

_____

_____

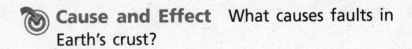

Cause and Effect What causes faults in Earth's crust?

_____

Draw a picture illustrating one of the words on this page.

convection (kahn VEHK shuhn) the transfer of thermal energy by the mass movement of particles in a liquid or gas

convección transferencia de energía térmica mediante el movimiento de masa de las partículas que hay en un líquido o gas

convection current a current caused by convection that drives fluid through a circular path

corriente de convección corriente causada por la convección que impulsa los fluidos a través de un recorrido circular

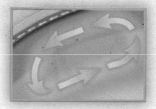

fault a crack in Earth's crust along which movement takes place

falla grieta en la corteza terrestre a lo largo de la cual hay movimiento

fossil the preserved remains or traces of an organism that lived in the distant past

fósil restos o huellas que se conservan de un organismo que vivió en el pasado lejano

magma hot melted rock below Earth's surface

magma roca fundida caliente que hay bajo la superficie de la Tierra

Glossary

plate boundary the edge of a tectonic plate

> **límite de la placa** borde de una placa tectónica

sea-floor spreading a process in which magma wells up and fills the space between spreading tectonic plates

> **relleno del lecho marino** proceso mediante el cual el magma sube y rellena el espacio entre las placas tectónicas

strata horizontal layers of rock

> **estratos** capas horizontales de roca

subduction a geologic process in which one tectonic plate sinks beneath another

> **sustracción** proceso geológico en el que una placa tectónica se hunde bajo otra

tectonic plate a giant slab of lithosphere that floats on Earth's mantle

> **placa tectónica** bloque gigantesco de litosfera que flota sobre el manto

 Visit www.eduplace.com to play puzzles and word games.

Circle the word in this glossary that is the same in English and Spanish.

Chapter Review

WHAT DID YOU LEARN?

Vocabulary

❶ (Circle) the correct answer on the page.

Comprehension

❷ _____
_____

❸ _____
_____

_____
❹ _____
_____

_____

Critical Thinking

❺ _____
_____

_____

Responding

Think About What You Have Read

Vocabulary

❶ Tectonic plates float above the _____.

  A) crust

  B) core

  C) asthenosphere

  D) ocean

Comprehension

❷ What evidence does a fossil provide?

❸ What would happen to tectonic plates if Earth's interior cooled?

❹ What creates volcanoes in the Ring of Fire?

Critical Thinking

❺ What question would you ask if you were interviewing a scientist who measured rates of plate movement?

WHAT DO YOU KNOW?

List one fact about each of these topics:

a. How mountains form _____

_____

_____

b. What happens during an earthquake _____

_____

_____

c. How volcanoes form _____

_____

_____

Mountains, Earthquakes, and Volcanoes

Contents

WHAT DO YOU WANT TO KNOW?

Skim the pictures and headings in this chapter. List one thing you want to find out about each of the following events.

Mountain Building: _____

_____

_____

Earthquakes: _____

_____

_____

Volcanoes: _____

_____

_____

_____

VOCABULARY

dome mountain a dome-shaped mound that forms when magma rises toward the surface but doesn't break through Earth's crust *(noun)*

fault-block mountain a mountain that forms from a block of crust that is pushed upward or downward along a fault *(noun)*

fold mountain a mountain that forms where continental plates collide, causing the crust to fold and crumble *(noun)*

hot spot an area of the crust above a rising plume of magma, where volcanic material can erupt through a plate, creating volcanic mountains *(noun)*

volcano an opening in Earth's crust through which melted rock, hot gases, rock fragments, and ash reach the surface *(noun)*

VOCABULARY SKILL: Word Content

Range is used to describe a group of mountains. *Range* has other meanings, too. Think about some of those meanings. Write one of them here.

_____

_____

_____

1.e. Students know that major geologic events result from plate motions.
1.f. Students can explain major features of California geology in terms of plate tectonics.

1 How Do Mountains Form?

Mountains form from plate motions.

Folding and Faulting Forces

Mountains are Earth's tallest landforms. You might think something so large never changes, but this is not true. Mountains can be formed and destroyed. The action of tectonic plates forms mountains. Weathering and erosion can wear mountains down.

There are five basic types of mountains. They are fold, fault-block, volcanic, dome, and erosion mountains. Most mountains form near plate boundaries. A **fold mountain** forms at the place where continental plates crash together. The crust folds and crumples and a mountain rises up.

Continental plates crash together and folding takes place. This action makes mountains.

Faulting can form huge cliffs. A large section of rock is forced up or down.

Erosion wears down the folds of a mountain. Some of the oldest fold mountains have rounded peaks.

Stress on the crust can cause it to crack instead of fold. This makes faults, or breaks, in the crust. A **fault-block mountain** forms from a block of crust that is pushed up or down along a fault.

Erosion helps shape fault-block mountains. Valleys are sometimes partly filled with rocks that have eroded from nearby mountains.

1. List the five basic types of mountains.

   a. _____

   b. _____

   c. _____

   d. _____

   e. _____

2. Complete the table to compare fold and fault-block mountains.

Type of Mountain	How It Forms	How Erosion Changes It
Fold		
Fault-block		

99

3. Complete the diagram to explain how volcanoes form at convergent boundaries.

> Two plates come together at a convergent boundary.

↓

> One plate _____ into the mantle and melts, forming _____.

↓

> Later, the _____ rises and bursts through the crust. It forms a _____.

4. Tell how volcanic mountains can form at divergent boundaries.

_____

_____

_____

Volcanic Forces

Some volcanoes erupt in fiery explosions. Other volcanoes do not erupt. **Volcanoes** are mountains formed by magma that came from inside Earth to the surface. The magma cooled and became a mountain.

Volcanic activity usually happens at convergent boundaries. A plate sinks into the mantle and melts. Later, the magma may rise and burst through the crust. It can build up over time to form a volcanic mountain.

At divergent boundaries, two plates pull apart. Magma rises up in the gap and cools. It builds up to form mountains like the Mid-Atlantic Ridge.

Volcanic mountains can also form away from plate boundaries. Magma plumes rising from the mantle make **hot spots** under some areas of the crust. When a plate moves over the hot spot, volcanic material can break through the plate. This makes a volcanic mountain.

Sometimes magma pushes against Earth's crust but does not break through. When this happens, a dome mountain is formed. A **dome mountain** is a rounded or dome-shaped mound that forms in Earth's crust.

Hardened magma

Dome mountains form when volcanic material pushes up from under the crust.

5. Compare and contrast volcanic mountains formed at hot spots with those formed at convergent boundaries.

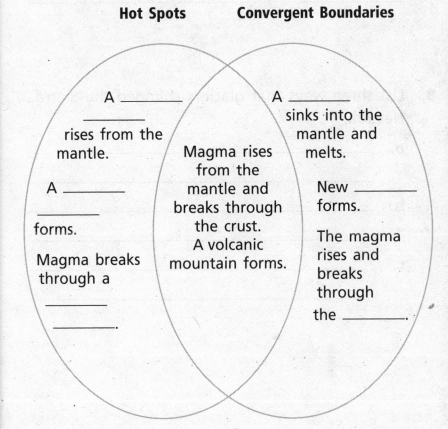

Hot Spots

A _____ _____ rises from the mantle.

A _____ _____ forms.

Magma breaks through a _____.

Convergent Boundaries

A _____ sinks into the mantle and melts.

New _____ forms.

The magma rises and breaks through the _____.

Magma rises from the mantle and breaks through the crust. A volcanic mountain forms.

6. When magma pushes against the crust but does not break through, a _____ forms.

7. What are erosion mountains?

_____

_____

8. List three ways that glaciers changed the Sierra Nevada.

a. _____

_____

b. _____

_____

c. _____

_____

Erosion Mountains

Weathering and erosion are always changing the shape of Earth's landforms. Some mountains were built entirely by the forces of erosion and weathering. These mountains are called erosion mountains.

The Catskills in New York are one example of erosion mountains. Glaciers carved a plateau into peaks and valleys. Rushing streams sculpted the land.

Erosion shapes some mountains after they are formed. These mountains often have peaks and valleys that are different sizes and shapes.

California's largest mountain range is the Sierra Nevada. These fault-block mountains were shaped by erosion. Glaciers eroded the peaks. They carved out bowls in the land, which are now filled with small or large lakes.

Glaciers made V-shaped valleys wider. The valleys in parts of the Sierra Nevada now look like U-shaped valleys.

Glaciers, rivers, and gravity all helped shape the rolling hills of the Catskills.

Erosion on this mountain has stripped plants and trees away from the rock layers.

I Wonder . . . Why is a mountain with a sharp, jagged peak probably younger than a mountain with a rounded peak?

_____

_____

_____

_____

_____

_____

_____

Summary There are five types of mountains. Many are formed from plate motions. Others form from weathering and erosion.

List three types of mountains found in California.

a. _____

b. _____

c. _____

Describe two processes that have shaped California's mountains.

_____

_____

_____

Classify How are dome mountains different from most other mountains?

_____

_____

California Mountains

Most of California is on the North American Plate. Some of western California is on the Pacific Plate. The movements of these plates have shaped the mountains in California.

The Sierra Nevada chain is a huge range of fault-block mountains. Mount Shasta and Lassen Peak are volcanic mountains. They are part of the Cascades. Other mountain ranges in California are fold mountains.

The mountains in California provide recreation and beauty.

CLASSIFY

How are dome mountains different from most other mountains?

What Happens During an Earthquake?

Earthquakes are caused by sudden motions along breaks in the crust.

At the Faults

Movements in Earth's crust are usually very small and slow. But sometimes these movements can be quick and violent. These quick movements cause sudden changes to Earth's surface.

Earthquakes are one of these sudden changes. Movement takes place along faults, which are usually located along plate boundaries. Stress builds up in rocks along faults and causes earthquakes.

This freeway in California was broken apart by an earthquake.

VOCABULARY

seismic wave a wave that carries energy released by an earthquake; the waves travel in all directions, including up to the surface *(noun)*

seismograph a tool for recording seismic waves *(noun)*

VOCABULARY SKILL: Word Origins

The words *seismic wave* and *seismograph* both have *seis* as their root. These words are related to the Greek word *seiein*, which means "to shake." Tell how this root word relates to the meaning of *seismic wave* and *seismograph*.

_____

_____

_____

_____

1.d. Students can define earthquakes and volcanoes.
3.a. Students know that energy can be carried from one place to another.

1. What causes an earthquake?

_____

_____

2. List the three types of faults and how the ground along each type of fault moves.

a. _____

_____

b. _____

_____

c. _____

_____

3. Look back at your list. (Circle) how the San Andreas Fault moves.

Types of Faults

Faults can be divided into three main groups. The groups are based on the type of force that forms the faults. There are also differences in the way faults move.

Normal faults take place at or near divergent boundaries. Earth's crust is stretched apart, and the rock breaks. A fault forms when one block moves down along a sloping crack. Volcanoes and earthquakes are common along normal faults.

Reverse faults usually happen at convergent plate boundaries. The rock is squeezed and then it breaks. One block is pushed up along a sloping crack. One plate may subduct, or go under, the other. Mountains and trenches are often made at reverse faults.

Tectonic plates slide past each other horizontally at transform-fault boundaries. This is where strike-slip faults occur. The blocks move horizontally. The rock in one block grinds against the other. Look at the diagram on page 107 to see the horizontal movement in this type of fault. The San Andreas Fault in California is a strike-slip fault.

Different Types of Faults

NORMAL Sections of crust in a normal fault move apart. The rock snaps and one block moves down.

REVERSE Rocks are squeezed as they come together. One block moves up as the other moves down.

STRIKE-SLIP Rocks move horizontally and grind against each other. Pressure builds up and the rocks break.

4. Complete the chart to tell about faults.

Type of Fault	Where It Occurs
Normal fault	At or near _____, places where Earth's crust is being
Reverse fault	At _____, where rock is being _____
Strike-slip fault	Where tectonic plates _____ at _____ boundaries

5. In which direction do seismic waves travel?

_____

6. (Circle) the word that makes the statement true.

Seismic waves become (weaker, stronger) as they move away from the center of an earthquake.

I Wonder . . . How are seismic waves similar to ripples from a stone dropped into the water? What do you think?

_____

_____

_____

Seismic Waves

Sometimes rocks jam up against tectonic plates. Rocks can get stuck between two plates. This causes stress to build up within the rock.

After some time the stress causes the rock to break. The plates shudder and jolt into a new place. This causes an earthquake.

Earthquakes release energy that travels in waves. These waves go in all directions, even up to the surface. These waves are called **seismic waves** (SYZ mihk wayvs). Sesmic waves become weaker as they move away from the center of the earthquake.

This is a longitudinal wave. It is like a P-wave. The wave travels back and forth through the spring.

The rope moves up and down as the wave travels through it. This is like an S-wave.

Body Waves Seismic waves that travel inside Earth are called body waves. There are two kinds of body waves. The first are called primary waves, or P-waves. They are the fastest waves. The first jolt of an earthquake is caused by the P-waves. The P-waves push and pull on rock along their path. Rocks move back and forth in the same direction that the P-waves travel.

The second type of body wave is the S-wave. S-waves are secondary waves. They arrive after the P-waves in an earthquake. S-waves cause rock to move up and down or side to side.

7. There are two kinds of seismic body waves. Identify each type of body wave shown. Then complete the sentences.

a. Type of wave: _____
During an earthquake, rocks move _____, in the same direction that this wave travels.

b. Type of wave: _____
During an earthquake, rocks move _____ or _____.

8. Tell which type of wave each statement describes. Write *P*-wave, *S*-wave, or *L*-wave in each space. Some statements apply to more than one type of wave.

_____ This type of wave is a seismic wave.

_____ This type of wave is a body wave.

_____ This type of wave produces a rolling motion across the surface and causes a lot of damage.

_____ This type of wave arrives first in an earthquake.

_____ This type of wave can travel through both solids and liquids.

_____ This type of wave arrives second.

_____ This type of wave travels the slowest.

P-waves can travel through solids and liquids. They can travel through Earth's liquid outer core. S-waves can only travel through solid rock.

Other waves travel only across Earth's surface. These are the third group of waves and are called L-waves. L-waves travel the slowest. They hit after both P-waves and S-waves.

L-waves cause a rolling motion on the surface of Earth. This motion can cause a lot of damage to houses and other buildings. L-waves often cause the worst damage.

All seismic waves travel very fast. There are ways to prepare for earthquakes, but there is no way to stop them from happening.

Seismic Waves

P-WAVES
P-waves are the first to arrive at the surface. They are longitudinal waves.

S-WAVES
S-waves come next. They are transverse waves.

L-WAVES
L-waves are a type of surface wave. These are usually very destructive.

Recording Seismic Waves

Scientists can find the starting point of an earthquake and measure its strength. A **seismograph** finds and measures the amount of ground motion during an earthquake. Seismographs are the main tool for measuring the strength of an earthquake. They can also tell how long the earthquake lasted.

A seismograph also records a written report of seismic waves called a seismogram. Seismographs also record aftershocks. Aftershocks are smaller earthquakes that follow the first one.

On a seismogram, P-waves appear first, S-waves appear second, and surface waves come last.

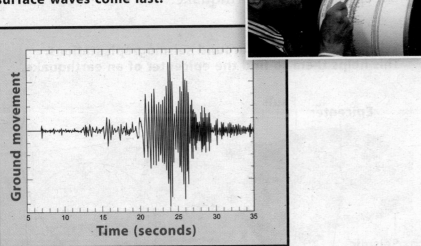

Summary Earthquakes are caused by sudden motions of the crust along faults. What tool do scientists use to record the strength and duration of seismic waves caused by earthquakes?

🎯 **Cause and Effect** What happens when stresses build up along a fault?

Cause		Effect
Stresses build up along a fault.	→	

CAUSE AND EFFECT

What happens when stresses build up along a fault?

111

VOCABULARY

epicenter the point on the surface directly above the focus of an earthquake *(noun)*

focus the point underground where an earthquake begins *(noun)*

intensity a measure of the amount of ground shaking an earthquake produces *(noun)*

magnitude a measure of the amount of energy that an earthquake releases *(noun)*

tsunami a huge sea wave produced by an earthquake, landslide, or volcanic eruption on the ocean floor *(noun)*

VOCABULARY SKILL: Word Parts

The word part *epi-* sometimes means "over." Explain how this meaning of *epi-* helps you understand the meaning of the word *epicenter*.

_____

_____

_____

1.g. Students can determine the epicenter of an earthquake and list the factors that affect the damage caused by an earthquake.
2.d. Students know that natural events change human and wildlife habitats.

3 How Are Earthquakes Located and Measured?

Scientists can measure the strength of an earthquake. Earthquakes damage human and wildlife habitats.

Focus and Epicenter

Scientists can find the center of an earthquake right when it strikes. The **focus** of an earthquake is the point underground where the earthquake begins.

The point on the surface right above the focus is called the **epicenter**. The epicenter is usually where the earthquake is felt most strongly. It is also the place where the damage is greatest.

Scientists study data from seismographs to find the epicenter. They compare S-waves and P-waves to find the epicenter of an earthquake.

Scientists draw circles around seismograph stations. This helps them to find the epicenter of an earthquake.

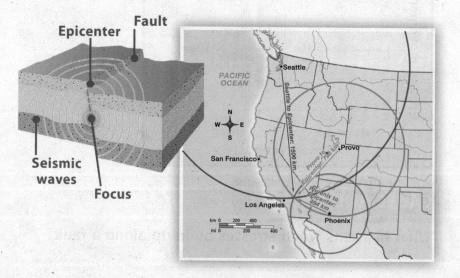

Modified Mercalli Scale

Scale	Observations
I to III	Minimally felt
IV	Felt indoors, like a heavy truck passing by
V	Felt by all, trees and poles shake
VI	Moves furniture, loosens plaster
VII	Damages poorly built houses and buildings
VIII	Damages most buildings, walls collapse
IX	Cracks appear in ground, mass destruction, landslides
X	Ground badly cracked, buildings and foundations destroyed
XI to XII	Total destruction, waves seen on ground

Measuring Earthquakes

Some earthquakes release a huge amount of energy. Other earthquakes are smaller, and release very little energy. The amount of energy an earthquakes releases depends on how much rock breaks. It also depends on how far rocks move.

There are two ways to measure the energy released by an earthquake. The first is **intensity**—a measure of the amount of damage the earthquake causes.

The Modified Mercalli scale is the most common way to measure intensity. Read the table of the scale shown above.

1. Explain how the focus and the epicenter of an earthquake are related.

_____

_____

_____

_____

2. List two things that affect the amount of energy an earthquake releases.

   a. _____

   b. _____

3. The _____ of an earthquake is a measure of the amount of damage the earthquake causes.

4. The _____ of an earthquake is a measure of the amount of energy the earthquake releases.

5. Compare and contrast the Modified Mercalli scale and the Richter scale. List two differences for each scale.

Measuring Earthquakes

Modified Mercalli Scale   **Richter Scale**

Charles Richter came up with the Richter scale to measure earthquake magnitude. **Magnitude** is the amount of energy that an earthquake releases.

The Richter scale is based on seismograph readings. Each number stands for a 10-fold increase in ground shaking. This means that in a magnitude 6 earthquake the ground shakes 10 times as much as it would in a magnitude 5 earthquake.

The table on this page shows the major earthquakes that have struck California, along with the magnitude of each.

Major Earthquakes in California	
Richter Scale	**Place and Date of Earthquake**
8.25	San Francisco; April 18, 1906
7.4	Yucca Valley; June 28, 1992
7.1	Loma Prieta; Oct. 17–18, 1989
6.7	Northridge; Jan. 17, 1994
6.6	Superstition Hills; Nov. 24, 1987

Four out of California's five largest earthquakes happened in the late 1980s and early 1990s.

Effects of Earthquakes

The most serious earthquakes cause landslides and destroy plants, animals, and their habitats. Earthquakes that strike cities damage buildings and crack open gas and water mains. They also can start fires, destroy trees, and bring down power lines.

The shaking an earthquake causes is strongest at the epicenter. Farther away from the epicenter, the shaking is not as strong. The amount of damage done depends on the strength of an earthquake and how long it lasts.

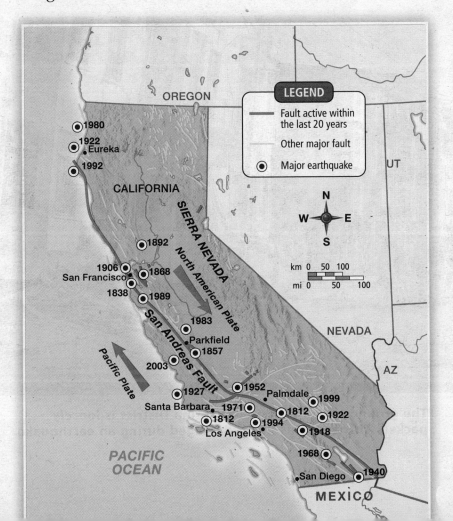

6. Describe the kinds of damage caused by a strong earthquake.

_____

_____

_____

_____

_____

7. The black dots on the map show the epicenters of some California earthquakes. Trace the San Andreas Fault with your finger. Where do most earthquakes happen in California?

_____

_____

_____

I Wonder . . . Why might a home built on land reclaimed from a bay suffer more damage than a similar home built on hard bedrock near the epicenter of an earthquake? What do you think?

_____

_____

_____

_____

_____

_____

The amount of damage an earthquake causes also depends on what the ground is like. Shaking is more intense on ground with loose or soft soil. An area of hard bedrock close to the epicenter might not suffer as much damage.

In 1989, the Loma Prieta earthquake struck San Francisco. Rock and soil had been dumped into the San Francisco Bay. This area was called the Marina District. When the earthquake hit, this area had more damage than other parts of the city.

The ground in San Francisco's Marina District is loosely packed. This area was badly damaged during an earthquake.

A triangle-shaped framework helps this building stand during an earthquake.

Preparing for Earthquakes

Today, structures in California are built to stay standing during an earthquake. Small buildings are anchored to their foundations. Concrete-covered steel rods make walls stronger.

Special foundations cushion buildings against shocks. And buildings are made of flexible materials, such as wood, instead of bricks that can break and crumble.

If you are inside during an earthquake, stand under a door frame or duck under a table. Stay away from windows and walls. If you are outside during an earthquake, move away from buildings, power lines, and tall trees.

8. Complete the diagram to tell how to keep safe during an earthquake.

Stay Safe in an Earthquake

Inside:
- Duck _____ or stand _____.
- Stay away from _____ and _____.

Outside:
- Move away from _____, _____, and _____.

Summary Earthquakes can be located and measured. Earthquakes damage human and wildlife habitats. List three things that affect how much damage an earthquake causes.

a. _____

b. _____

c. _____

 Main Idea What causes a tsunami?

Cause		Effect
_____ _____ _____ _____	→	A huge sea wave forms.

The Indian Ocean tsunami of 2004 was one of the worst disasters in history.

In 1946, an earthquake in Alaska caused a tsunami in Hawaii, which was 5,000 kilometers away!

Alaska

0   600   1200 miles
0   600   1200 kilometers

Tsunamis

Earthquakes can strike under the ocean. They can cause a **tsunami** (su NAH mee), a huge sea wave produced by an earthquake, a landslide, or a volcanic eruption on the ocean floor.

A tsunami cannot be noticed in deep water in the middle of the ocean. The waves rise as they approach the shallow coast. The giant waves strike the shore, sweeping people and buildings away.

The worst tsunami was in the Indian Ocean in 2004. Today, scientists use tsunameters to predict tsunamis. There is a tsunameter in the Pacific Ocean, but the Indian Ocean does not have one yet.

MAIN IDEA

What causes a tsunami?

How Do Volcanoes Form?

4

Volcanoes form where magma reaches Earth's surface.

Inside a Volcano

A volcano is an opening in Earth's crust through which melted rock, hot gases, rock fragments, and ash reach the surface. The melted rock under Earth's surface is magma. Gas-filled magma rises to the surface of a volcano.

Magma can burst through an opening in the crust as lava. **Lava** is magma that reaches Earth's surface. Cooling lava builds up and forms a volcanic mountain.

Other materials can also burst out of a volcano. Rock pieces, dust, ash, steam, and gases pour out and burn anything in their path.

VOCABULARY

cinder cone volcano a volcano with slopes made mostly of rock and ash *(noun)*

composite volcano a volcano composed of alternating layers of lava and ash *(noun)*

island arc a string of volcanic islands that form where one oceanic plate sinks beneath another *(noun)*

lava magma that flows onto Earth's surface from a volcano *(noun)*

shield volcano a volcano that has a gentle slope and is made almost entirely of layers of lava *(noun)*

VOCABULARY SKILL: Word Origins

Vulcan was the blacksmith of the Roman gods. It was believed he had a fiery forge deep inside Earth, with a chimney that spewed heat, ash, and lava. Tell how you think the name *Vulcan* relates to the word *volcano*.

_____

_____

_____

 1.d. Students can define earthquakes and volcanoes.
2.d. Students know that natural events change human and wildlife habitats.

119

1. Compare and contrast magma and lava.

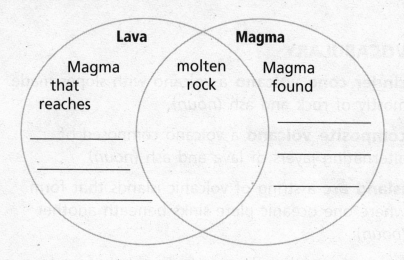

Lava — Magma that reaches _____ _____ _____

molten rock

Magma — Magma found _____ _____ _____

2. Complete the sentences to explain how an island arc forms.

a. Two _____ plates meet.

b. One plate _____ under the other and _____.

c. Volcanoes erupt and build up from the _____.

d. The volcanoes form a _____ called an island arc.

Volcanoes and Plate Tectonics

Volcanoes can be found grouped together in some areas. They are common around the rim of the Pacific Ocean. This area is called the Ring of Fire.

Volcanoes often form at convergent plate boundaries. When an ocean plate and a continental plate meet, the ocean plate is pushed under the land plate and melts. This causes a volcano to form.

When two oceanic plates meet, one plate dives under the other. All along this subduction zone, underwater volcanoes form from rising magma. A string of volcanic islands may build up, called an **island arc**.

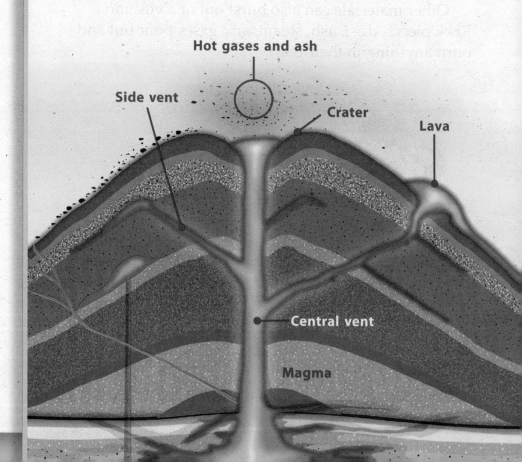

Hot gases and ash

Side vent

Crater

Lava

Central vent

Magma

Classifying Volcanoes

Not all volcanoes are alike. Volcanoes can be different sizes, and they erupt in different ways. The lava's thickness and the amount of gases in it are also different. Volcanoes are grouped by type of eruption, shape, and structure. There are three main groups of volcanoes.

Cinder Cone Volcanoes A **cinder cone volcano** is a volcano with slopes made mostly of rock and ash. Cinder cones are the smallest volcanoes. Most have deep craters, or holes, at the top. Cinder cone volcanoes are usually made by just one eruption.

CINDER CONE VOLCANO
A single eruption piled these ashes into a cone shape.

Crater

Layers of ash

Central vent filled with rock fragments

3. List three characteristics by which volcanoes are grouped.

a. _____

b. _____

c. _____

4. Look at the picture of the cinder cone volcano. These are the smallest types of volcanoes. Fill in the table below to summarize the characteristics of cinder cone volcanoes.

Cinder Cone Volcanoes	
Type of eruption	
Shape	
Structure	

5. Look at the picture of the composite volcano. Find the layers of ash and lava. Fill in the table below to summarize the characteristics of composite volcanoes.

Composite Volcanoes	
Type of eruption	
Shape	
Structure	

6. Explain why composite volcanoes sometimes have violent eruptions.

_____

_____

_____

Composite Volcanoes A **composite volcano** is composed of alternating layers of lava and ash. Composite volcanoes are shaped like a cone. They have steep slopes. Each eruption of a composite volcano adds another layer of volcanic material to its slope.

Composite volcanoes have thick lava. The lava traps gas under the volcano. When the gas is released, it often causes violent eruptions.

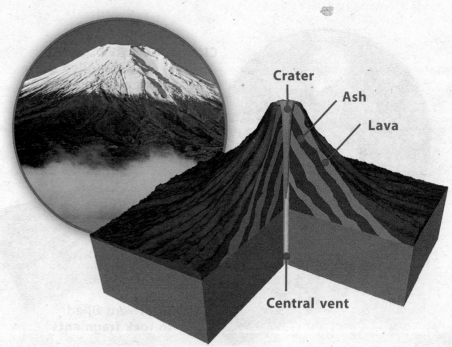

COMPOSITE VOLCANO Each eruption adds a new layer along the slope. Mount Fuji in Japan last erupted in 1707.

Shield Volcanoes A **shield volcano** is made of layers and layers of lava. It has gentle slopes and many vents, or openings. This type of volcano has thin, smooth lava that flows quickly. The shield volcano is the largest type of volcano.

Scientists describe volcanoes as active, dormant, or extinct. An active volcano has erupted recently or may erupt soon. (In the life of a volcano, that means a few hundred years!)

A dormant volcano is not active, but could become active someday. An extinct volcano is not likely to erupt again.

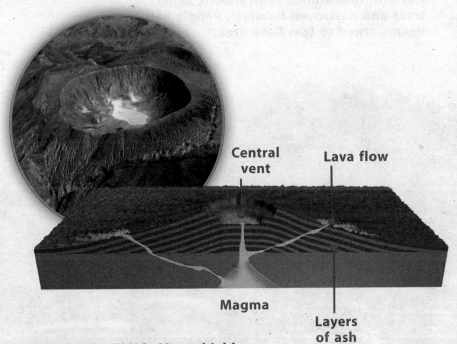

Central vent

Lava flow

Magma

Layers of ash

SHIELD VOLCANO Most shield volcanoes have bases on the ocean floor. The islands of Hawaii are all shield volcanoes.

7. Look at the picture of the shield volcano. These large volcanoes are the type of volcano you would find in Hawaii. Fill in the table below to summarize the characteristics of shield volcanoes.

Shield Volcanoes	
Type of eruption	
Shape	
Structure	

8. Explain each of the following terms.
   a. active volcano: _____
   _____
   b. dormant volcano: _____
   _____
   c. extinct volcano: _____
   _____

9. Complete each list to describe the effects of volcanic eruptions.

> Volcanic eruptions can quickly change
>
> Earth's surface.

Harmful changes to wildlife habitats

a. _____

b. _____

c. _____

Harmful changes to human habitats

a. _____

b. _____

_____

I Wonder . . . You read about a volcanic eruption in the Philippines. The volcano exploded violently and sent lava down its sides and ash into the air. What kind of volcano do you think this is?

_____

_____

_____

_____

Effects of Volcanoes

Volcanic eruptions can quickly change Earth's surface. They can be harmful to people who live near them. Volcanic eruptions can set fire to forests and expel hot and poisonous gases. They can kill wildlife and bury their habitats—even destroy whole cities.

Scientists watch many active volcanoes around the world. They study seismographs and measure physical changes in the land. They can predict when a volcanic eruption might happen.

Hot ash from Mount Saint Helens killed trees and destroyed habitats. People had been warned to leave the area.

California's Volcanoes

California's largest volcanoes are two mountains of the Cascade range. One is called Mount Shasta and the other is Lassen Peak. Mount Saint Helens in Washington is also in this chain of mountains.

Mount Shasta has not erupted for more than 200 years. Lassen Peak released steam, ash, and lava in many eruptions between 1914 and 1921. Lava swept away some buildings, and hot gases burned trees. There were few towns or people in the area, so not much damage was done. That was the last time a volcano erupted in California.

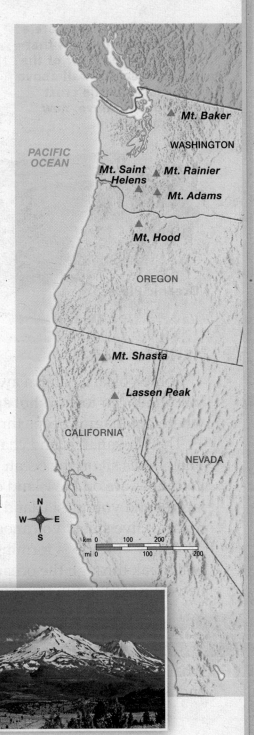

The map shows several volcanic mountains of the Cascade Range. California's Mount Shasta is in Siskiyou County, close to the Oregon border.

10. Find Mount Shasta and Lassen Peak on the map. In which mountain range are these two California volcanoes located?

_____

11. Why did the Lassen Peak eruptions between 1914 and 1921 do little damage to human habitats?

_____

_____

I Wonder . . . Mount Lassen last erupted in 1921. Is this volcano active, dormant, or extinct? What do you think?

_____

_____

_____

125

Summary   Volcanoes form where magma reaches Earth's surface. The three common types of volcanoes are cinder cone, composite, and shield volcanoes. Tell what kind of volcanoes make up the Hawaiian Islands and how these islands form.

_____

_____

_____

◎ **Compare and Contrast**   What is the difference between a dormant volcano and an extinct one?

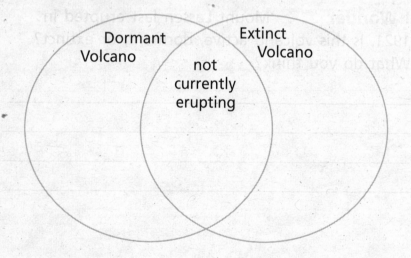

Dormant Volcano

Extinct Volcano

not currently erupting

The Hawaiian Islands are a series of shield cones that reach from the floor of the Pacific Ocean to well above its surface. As the crust continues to move, new mountains form.

Oceanic Plate

Mantle

Hawaiian Islands

Some volcanoes form away from plate edges. Volcanoes can form at hot spots. A hot spot is an area where hot magma seeps through Earth's crust.

The Hawaiian island chain is a string of volcanoes. Their bases sit on the ocean floor. Today, the only active volcanoes are on the island of Hawaii. This is the largest and youngest island of the chain. This island is made of five shield volcanoes that grew together.

A new volcano is forming near Hawaii. One day it will break through the ocean's surface and become the newest island in the Hawaiian chain.

COMPARE AND CONTRAST

What is the difference between a dormant volcano and an extinct one?

cinder cone volcano a volcano with slopes made mostly of rock and ash

    cono volcánico montaña cuyas laderas están formadas en su mayor parte por roca y ceniza volcánica

composite volcano a volcano composed of alternating layers of lava and ash

    volcán compuesto volcán compuesto de capas alternas de lava y ceniza

dome mountain a dome-shaped mound that forms when magma rises toward the surface but doesn't break through Earth's crust

    montaña volcánica monte con forma de cúpula que se forma cuando el magma alcanza la superficie de la Tierra pero no rompe la corteza

epicenter the point on the surface directly above the focus of an earthquake

    epicentro punto que en la superficie está directamente sobre el foco de un terremoto

fault-block mountain a mountain that forms from a block of crust that is pushed upward or downward along a fault

    montaña entre fallas montaña que se forma por un bloque de corteza que es empujado verticalmente a lo largo de una falla

focus the point underground where an earthquake begins

    foco punto bajo tierra donde comienza un terremoto

Group two of the words on this page and explain why they go together.

_____

_____

_____

_____

Write a sentence that uses the words *lava* and *island arc*.

_____

_____

_____

_____

fold mountain a mountain that forms where continental plates collide, causing the crust to fold and crumble

montaña plegada montaña que se forma donde colisionan las placas continentales, haciendo que la corteza se doble y se derrumbe

hot spot an area of the crust above a rising plume of magma, where volcanic material can erupt through a plate, creating volcanic mountains

punto caliente zona de la corteza situada sobre una columna de magma, donde es posible que el material volcánico salga a través de una placa, creando una montaña volcánica

intensity a measure of the amount of ground shaking an earthquake produces

intensidad medida de la cantidad de temblores de tierra producidos por un terremoto

island arc a string of volcanic islands that form where one oceanic plate sinks beneath another

arco de islas conjunto de islas volcánicas que se forman cuando una placa oceánica se hunde debajo de otra

lava magma that flows onto Earth's surface from a volcano

lava magma que sale de un volcán a la superficie de la Tierra

Glossary

magnitude a measure of the amount of energy that an earthquake releases

magnitud cantidad de energía que libera un terremoto

seismic wave (SYZ mihk wayv) a wave that carries energy released by an earthquake in all directions, including up to the surface

onda sísmica onda que carga energía liberada por un terremoto, y que viaja en todas direcciones, incluso hacia la superficie

seismograph a tool for recording seismic waves

sismógrafo instrumento que registra las ondas sísmicas

shield volcano a volcano that has a gentle slope and is made almost entirely of layers of lava

volcán con apariencia de escudo volcán que tiene una pendiente suave formada casi por entero de capas de lava

tsunami (su NOM ee) a huge sea wave produced by an earthquake, landslide, or volcanic eruption on the ocean floor

maremoto gran ola marina producida por un terremoto, corrimiento de tierra o erupción volcánica en el suelo del océano

volcano an opening in Earth's crust through which melted rock, hot gases, rock fragments, and ash reach the surface

volcán abertura en la corteza terrestre a través de la cual salen a la superficie rocas fundidas, gases calientes, fragmentos de roca y cenizas

 Visit www.eduplace.com to play puzzles and word games.

Circle the word in this Glossary that is the same in English and Spanish.

129

Chapter Review

WHAT DID YOU LEARN?

Vocabulary

❶ Circle the correct answer on the page.

Comprehension

❷ _____

_____

_____

❸ _____

_____

_____

❹ _____

_____

_____

Critical Thinking

❺ _____

_____

_____

_____

Think About What You Have Read

Vocabulary

❶ Magma that reaches Earth's surface is _____.

 A) epicenter

 B) focus

 C) lava

 D) volcano

Comprehension

❷ Which two types of mountains are formed by the movement of magma?

❸ Compare the surface movements caused by P-waves and S-waves.

❹ What determines the amount of energy an earthquake releases?

Critical Thinking

❺ The state of California has passed laws that make it illegal for people to build homes near fault lines. Why do you think these laws were passed?

WHAT DO YOU KNOW?

List one fact about each of these topics:

a. How energy travels from the Sun to Earth

_____

_____

_____

b. How Earth is heated

_____

_____

_____

c. How heat energy is transferred

_____

_____

_____

Heating Earth

Contents

WHAT DO YOU WANT TO KNOW?

Skim the pictures and headings in this chapter. List one thing you want to find out about each of these topics:

a. How energy travels from the Sun to Earth

_____

_____

b. How Earth is heated

_____

_____

_____

c. How heat is transferred

_____

_____

_____

133

Lesson Preview

VOCABULARY

atmosphere the blanket of air that surrounds Earth *(noun)*

electromagnetic radiation energy transferred by waves that can travel through empty space *(noun)*

electromagnetic spectrum a continuous band that includes all types of electromagnetic radiation *(noun)*

wave a disturbance that transfers energy from one location to another *(noun)*

VOCABULARY SKILL: Word Origins

Atmosphere is formed from two Greek words—*atmos*, meaning "vapor," and *sphaira*, meaning "sphere," or "globe." Based on this information, tell what *atmosphere* means.

_____

_____

_____

134

1 How Does Energy Travel from the Sun to Earth?

Waves carry energy from one place to another. Energy from the Sun travels in waves called electromagnetic waves.

Waves and Energy

A **wave** is a motion that transfers energy from one location to another. Energy is the power to cause change or to do work. Waves carry energy but not matter.

When a wave travels through the ocean, the water molecules move for a moment. The motion that caused the wave is passed from one molecule to the next. Energy is passed through the ocean. The water itself does not move across the ocean.

Water waves, sound waves, and light waves all carry energy.

The Sun is Earth's main source of energy.

Sound waves are made when objects vibrate, or shake. Place your hand against your neck and make a noise. You can feel your vocal chords vibrating.

Light also travels in waves. Light waves can travel through a vacuum, which is empty space. Light waves move at the highest speed. Sound waves move more slowly.

The Sun produces light because it is very hot. The Sun is Earth's source of light. Light allows you to see. Plants use the energy of light to make food and to grow.

1. Complete the chart to tell about different energy waves.

Type of Wave	Feature	Example
_____	energy in the form of motion passed from one molecule of water to the next	_____
sound	_____ _____	alarm clock ringing
_____	can travel through a vacuum (empty space)	_____

2. Tell how each living thing uses light from the Sun.
   a. Animals and humans: _____
   _____
   b. Plants: _____
   _____

135

3. Fill in the blanks. Use the words *electromagnetic radiation* and *electromagnetic spectrum*.

a. Energy passed by waves that can travel through empty space is called _____
_____ .

b. A band that includes all types of electromagnetic radiation is called the _____ .

4. Read each clue. Tell the type of electromagnetic radiation that is being described.

Clue	Type of Radiation
have the longest wavelengths and carry the least energy	_____
have the shortest wavelengths and carry the most energy	_____
can be divided into its individual colors by a prism	_____

Electromagnetic Waves

What is light? Light is a type of electromagnetic radiation. **Electromagnetic radiation** is energy passed by waves that can travel through empty space. Other types of electromagnetic radiation are radio waves, microwaves, and x-rays.

Each type of energy has different properties, or qualities. These properties depend on the wavelength. Radio waves have the longest wavelengths and carry the least energy. Gamma rays have the shortest wavelengths and carry the most energy. Look at the diagram of wavelengths below.

The Electromagnetic Spectrum

Microwave ovens cook food using microwaves.

A toaster uses infrared waves to toast bread.

A radio picks up radio waves and makes sound.

Radio waves   **Microwaves**   **Infrared light**

Lower Energy

The Sun sends out waves across the entire **electromagnetic spectrum**. This is a band that includes all types of electromagnetic radiation. The diagram shows the electromagnetic spectrum.

Scientists can make and use different types of electromagnetic waves. Radio and television stations transmit information by using radio waves. Microwave ovens use microwaves to heat food. Toasters use infrared waves to toast bread. Doctors use x-rays to look inside the human body.

X-rays pass through soft tissues. They are used to take pictures of the body.

White light, or visible light, can be divided into its individual colors by a glass prism.

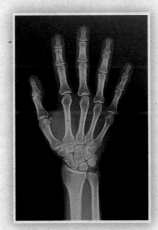

Visible light   Ultraviolet light   X-rays   Gamma rays

Higher Energy

5. Complete the diagram about the waves of the electromagnetic spectrum.

A radio picks up _____ and makes sound.

A microwave oven _____ using _____.

Uses of the Electromagnetic Spectrum

A toaster uses _____ to toast bread.

Doctors look inside the human body by using _____.

6. Complete each sentence to tell about visible light.

a. Visible light is also called _____.

b. Visible light is really made up of

_____

c. You can separate white light into colors by

using a _____.

d. Most of the Sun's radiation that reaches Earth's surface is in the form of

_____.

e. Other types of radiation are blocked

by Earth's _____.

I Wonder . . . Why don't you see rainbows when the weather is dry?

_____

_____

_____

_____

Visible Light

Visible light is also called white light. It is really made up of red, orange, yellow, green, blue, indigo, and violet. The colors form a band called the visible spectrum.

You can use a glass prism to separate white light into its colors. Sunlight entering tiny water droplets in the air is also separated into colors. That is how a rainbow forms!

Most of the radiation from the Sun that reaches Earth's surface is in the form of visible light. Other types of electromagnetic radiation are blocked by Earth's atmosphere. The **atmosphere** is the blanket of air that surrounds Earth.

Isaac Newton beamed white light through two prisms. He wrote a book about his experiments with visible light.

Sunscreen protects skin from too much ultraviolet light.

Ultraviolet and Infrared Light

Ultraviolet (UV) light carries more energy than visible light. It can harm humans and other organisms. Certain gases in Earth's atmosphere block much of the Sun's UV light from reaching the surface.

Some exposure to UV light is needed. It helps your body make vitamin D, which we need for healthy bones. But too much exposure can cause sunburn and eye damage. It can also cause early aging of the skin. Too much sun exposure may lead to skin cancer.

7. Complete the cause-and-effect diagram about ultraviolet light.

Cause	Effect
_____ _____	A person's body is able to make vitamin D, which is needed for healthy bones.
A person is exposed to too much UV light.	A person can develop a. _____ b. _____ c. _____ d. _____

Summary Waves carry energy from one place to another. Energy from the Sun travels through space as electromagnetic waves.

List three ways to stay safe from the Sun's UV radiation.

1. _____

_____

2. _____

_____

3. _____

_____

Sequence How do UV and IR radiation compare to visible light?

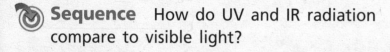

Infrared Light		Visible Light		Ultraviolet Light
_____	→		→	_____

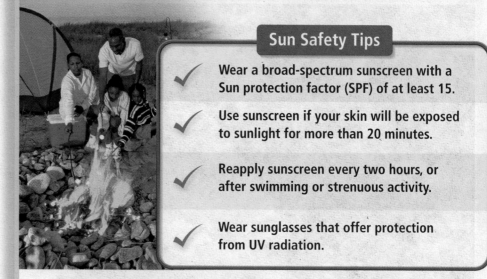

A campfire sends out infrared waves that warm the campers.

Read the Sun Safety Tips on the chart above. Going outdoors and being in the Sun is important for good health. It is also important to protect your skin.

The Sun also sends out infrared light. Most of Earth's atmosphere absorbs this light. Infrared (IR) light carries less energy than visible light. Your skin absorbs IR radiation. This causes your skin to feel warm. Infrared radiation is not harmful to humans.

SEQUENCE

How do UV and IR radiation compare to visible light?

140

How Is Earth Heated?

Energy from the Sun does not heat Earth evenly.

Uneven Heating

When sunlight strikes Earth, energy is absorbed by land, water, and the atmosphere. This energy is changed into thermal energy. Thermal energy heats Earth.

Earth has a range of different kinds of weather. It may be warm in California, cold in the far north, and steaming hot near the equator. This is because Earth is not heated evenly.

As you have learned, Earth rotates on its axis. Because the axis is tilted, Earth faces the Sun at an angle. Different parts of Earth get direct sunlight at different times of the year. The equator gets the most direct sunlight throughout the year. That means that areas near the equator have the greatest amount of solar energy. There is less solar energy farther away from the equator. This causes the differences in weather.

Arctic

Temperate

Equatorial

VOCABULARY

greenhouse effect the trapping of heat by certain gases in Earth's atmosphere *(noun)*

VOCABULARY SKILL: Word Phrases

You can sometimes figure out a phrase's meaning by studying the words that make up the phrase. A greenhouse is made of clear glass. Radiation from the Sun passes through the glass and heats the surfaces inside the greenhouse. The warmed surfaces give off heat in the form of infrared radiation. Glass lets very little infrared radiation pass through, so the heat is trapped inside. Now read the definition of *greenhouse effect*. How is the greenhouse effect similar to what happens in a greenhouse?

_____

_____

_____

4.b. Students know that energy travels from the Sun to Earth by radiation.

1. Complete the chart to explain how Earth's rotation affects the angle at which sunlight strikes the Earth.

> The angle of sunlight changes as the Sun changes ————————— in the sky.

↓

> At noon, sunlight strikes ————————— most directly.

↓

> In the morning and evening, sunlight strikes Earth at a —————————. This spreads solar energy over a greater area.

2. Look at the picture of the Sun's rays striking Earth. (Circle) California. Describe how the Sun's rays strike this area.

————————————————————

————————————————————

————————————————————

Because Earth's surface curves away from the equator, sunlight strikes the Earth at an increasingly smaller angle as you move north. As a result, the same amount of solar energy is spread out over a larger area. Another angle effect occurs because of Earth's rotation. As the Sun's position changes in the sky, the angle of sunlight changes. At noon, the sunlight strikes Earth most directly. In the morning and evening, sunlight strikes at a smaller angle, and solar energy is spread over a greater area.

When sunlight travels through the atmosphere at an angle, the light takes a longer path through the atmosphere. A longer path means that the light has a greater chance to be absorbed, reflected, or scattered. Less light reaches Earth's surface.

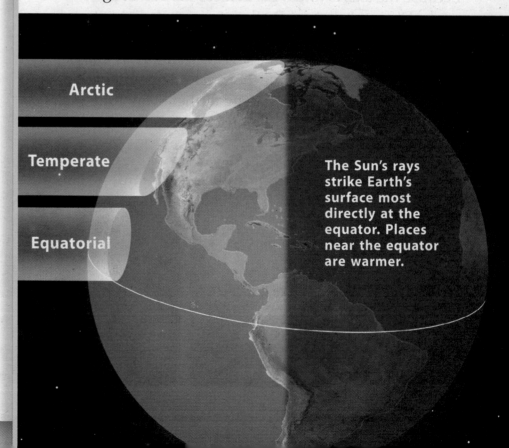

Arctic

Temperate

Equatorial

The Sun's rays strike Earth's surface most directly at the equator. Places near the equator are warmer.

Earth's Energy Balance

Earth receives only a small amount of the total energy that the Sun gives off. The small amount of energy that reaches Earth is still enough to power Earth's water cycle, create weather, and provide the energy that plants and other living things need to grow.

Sunlight strikes your skin and your skin feels warm. The sunlight is absorbed by your skin and changed into thermal energy. This happens to Earth's surface, too.

The diagram below shows how only some of the Sun's radiation reaches Earth's surface.

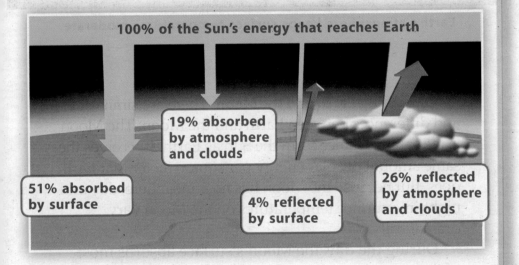

100% of the Sun's energy that reaches Earth

19% absorbed by atmosphere and clouds

51% absorbed by surface

4% reflected by surface

26% reflected by atmosphere and clouds

3. What percentage of the solar energy reaching Earth is reflected back into space?

_____

_____

4. Look at the diagram. Circle the percentages that tell the amount of energy that is absorbed by Earth's surface and by the atmosphere and clouds. What does this energy do?

_____

_____

_____

5. When sunlight strikes your skin or Earth's surface, it is absorbed and changed into

_____ energy.

143

6. Complete the diagram to compare and contrast Earth and the Moon.

Earth   **Moon**

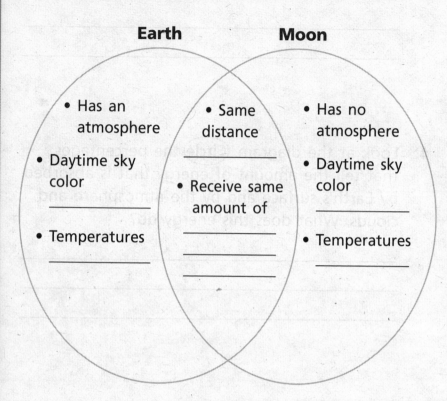

- Has an atmosphere
- Daytime sky color _____
- Temperatures _____

- Same distance _____
- Receive same amount of _____ _____

- Has no atmosphere
- Daytime sky color _____
- Temperatures _____

Earth

Earth's atmosphere keeps surface temperatures moderate.

Comparing Earth and the Moon There are similarities and differences between Earth and the Moon. The Moon is the same distance from the Sun as Earth. It receives the same amount of solar energy per square meter that Earth does. But because the Moon has no atmosphere, day and nighttime surface temperatures on the Moon vary dramatically.

During the day, the Moon's surface absorbs most of the incoming solar radiation. Because there's no atmosphere to reflect or absorb the heat, the surface becomes extremely hot. Daytime temperatures can reach 130°C (266°F)!

At night, with no atmosphere to trap heat, the Moon's surface quickly radiates infrared radiation into space. The surface temperature can plunge to –173° C (–279° F)!

On Earth, the sky looks blue during the day. The Moon's sky is black. This is another difference that can also be explained by atmosphere.

Light from the Sun scatters when it meets Earth's atmosphere. Blue light is scattered toward Earth's surface. This makes the sky appear blue. Because the Moon has no atmosphere, no sunlight scatters. The sky looks black.

Moon

The Moon does not have an atmosphere. It can be 130°C (266°F) during the day and -173°C (-279°F) at night.

I Wonder . . .   Why does the heat absorbed by the Moon during the day escape so quickly at night?

_____

_____

_____

145

7. Number the events below to describe the sequence of how the greenhouse effect occurs on Earth.

_____ The energy absorbed by the atmosphere is re-radiated back to Earth.

_____ Certain gases in the atmosphere allow radiation from the Sun to pass through and warm Earth's surface.

_____ The gases of the atmosphere absorb the energy from Earth's surface.

_____ Earth's warm surface sends energy back into the atmosphere.

8. _True or False?_ Life on Earth would not be possible without the greenhouse effect.

_____

The Greenhouse Effect

Certain gases in Earth's atmosphere allow radiation from the Sun to pass through. This radiation warms Earth's surfaces. The surface of Earth sends energy back into the atmosphere. This energy is absorbed by the gases there. It is sent in all directions, warming the surface of Earth and the lower atmosphere.

This way of warming the surface and lower atmosphere of a planet is known as the **greenhouse effect**. Life on Earth would be impossible without an atmosphere to make the greenhouse effect.

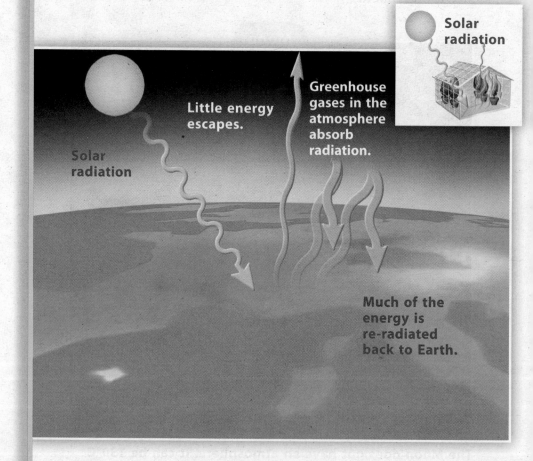

Solar radiation

Little energy escapes.

Greenhouse gases in the atmosphere absorb radiation.

Solar radiation

Much of the energy is re-radiated back to Earth.

The greenhouse effect depends on greenhouse gases in the atmosphere. Greenhouse gases trap solar energy and keep a planet warm.

Compare Earth to Venus. Venus has a very thick atmosphere. The atmosphere is mostly carbon dioxide. It traps most of the infrared radiation from Venus's surface and temperatures are very hot.

Mars has an atmosphere that is also mostly carbon dioxide. But Mars has a very thin atmosphere. Infrared radiation can easily escape into space and the temperatures are very cold.

Earth depends on a balance of greenhouse gases to maintain even temperatures. These temperatures support life on the planet.

Comparing Atmospheres

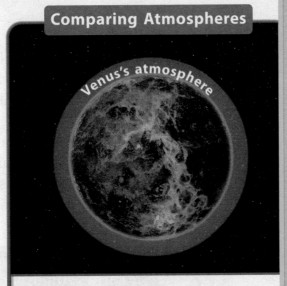

Venus has a thick atmosphere. This creates a greenhouse effect. The surface of Venus is very hot.

Mars has a thin atmosphere. There is almost no greenhouse effect. Temperatures on Mars can be very low.

9. Underline the correct words to compare the atmospheres of Venus and Mars.

Venus

- Very (thick, thin) atmosphere
- (More, less) carbon dioxide than Earth
- Traps more infrared radiation than Earth, so very (hot, cold)

Mars

- Very (thick, thin) atmosphere
- (More, less) carbon dioxide than Earth
- Traps less infrared radiation than Earth, so very (hot, cold)

I Wonder . . . How might an increase in the amount of carbon dioxide in the atmosphere affect Earth? What do you think?

_____

_____

_____

_____

147

10. Complete the diagram to tell about global warming.

Increased amounts of _____ trap heat.

Cutting down _____ increases _____.

Global Warming

As temperatures warm, _____ may melt.

If greehouse gases keep increasing, the planet could get _____.

Global Warming

Earth's average temperature has gone up over the past 100 years. This pattern is called global warming. Carbon dioxide and other greenhouse gases in Earth's atmosphere have also increased. The graph on this page shows the increase over the past 50 years.

Greenhouse gases trap heat and warm Earth's surface. If amounts of greenhouse gases keep going up, the planet could get warmer.

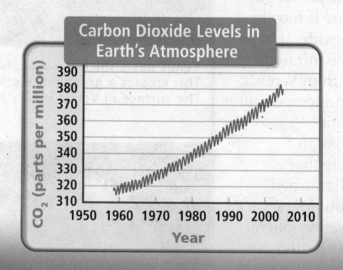

Carbon Dioxide Levels in Earth's Atmosphere

CO_2 (parts per million)

390
380
370
360
350
340
330
320
310

1950 1960 1970 1980 1990 2000 2010

Year

Scientists agree that human activity is the cause of more carbon dioxide in the atmosphere. Humans are cutting down forests, which absorb carbon dioxide as they grow and convert it to oxygen. Fewer plants and trees means more carbon dioxide will remain in the atmosphere.

If temperatures continue to go up, the ice sheets on Greenland and Antarctica could melt over time. Global ocean levels would rise as a result.

Scientists agree that global warming is happening and that human activity is causing it. Today, scientists and government leaders are discussing the possible consequences of global warming.

If global temperatures keep rising, much of Earth's ice could melt. In time, this could cause major flooding of coastal areas. The flooding could be so large that ocean-front cities someday could be totally under water.

COMPARE AND CONTRAST

Why are temperatures on Earth and the Moon so different?

Summary   Energy from the Sun does not heat Earth evenly. About half of the energy Earth receives is absorbed by the surface. Greenhouse gases help moderate Earth's surface temperature.

How are greenhouse gases and global warming related?

_____

_____

_____

Compare and Contrast   Why are temperatures on Earth and the Moon so different?

_____

_____

Lesson Preview

VOCABULARY

conduction the transfer of thermal energy by particle collision *(noun)*

convection the transfer of thermal energy by the mass movement of particles in a liquid or gas *(noun)*

convection current a current caused by convection that drives fluid through a circular path *(noun)*

density the amount of mass per unit volume of a substance *(noun)*

heat an amount of thermal energy transferred from a hotter object or region to a colder object or region *(noun)*

land breeze a cool wind blowing near the surface from land toward the sea *(noun)*

sea breeze the cool air that blows along the surface from the water toward land *(noun)*

temperature the average motion energy of particles in matter; a measure of hot or cold *(noun)*

thermal energy the total amount of motion energy from particles in matter *(noun)*

3.c. Students know that heat flows by conduction in solids and by conduction and convection in fluids.
4.d. Students know that convection currents distribute heat in the air and oceans.

150

---

3 What Are Convection Currents?

Thermal energy can be transferred by conduction, convection, or radiation.

Conduction and Convection

All matter is made of tiny particles that are always in motion. That motion makes energy. The *total* amount of motion energy from moving particles is called **thermal energy**. The *average* motion energy of the particles is the **temperature**. Temperature describes how hot or cold something is.

When a hot object is in contact with a cold object, thermal energy is always transferred from the hot object to the cold object. This transferred energy is called **heat**.

Thermal energy is transferred in this rod by conduction.

The movement of a gas or liquid, such as ocean water, transfers thermal energy in the process of convection.

Thermal energy is transferred by radiation, conduction, and convection. Radiation is the transfer of thermal energy by way of electromagnetic waves.

Conduction is the transfer of thermal energy by particle collision. The particles transfer energy but not matter.

Convection (kahn VEHK shuhn) is the transfer of thermal energy by mass movement of particles in a liquid or gas. Convection transports matter and energy.

1. Fill in the blanks to tell the difference between *temperature* and *thermal energy*.
   a. The total amount of motion energy from moving particles is called _____.
   b. The average motion energy of the particles is called _____.

2. Draw an arrow to show the direction in which heat will flow between these two objects.

Hot Object	Cold Object

3. Identify each type of thermal energy transfer.
   a. transfer by waves _____
   b. transfer by particle collision _____
   c. transfer by mass particle movement _____

151

4. Look at the photo of the aquarium. Trace the current with your finger. Complete the chart to describe this convection current.

> The heater warms water at one end of the aquarium. The water's density _____.

↓

> The warm water _____ to the surface and _____.

↓

> The water becomes _____ and _____.

↓

> The water reaches the _____, and the loop begins again.

Look at the picture of the aquarium. A heater warms the water in the aquarium. The water gets warmer and expands. Its density decreases. **Density** is the amount of mass per unit volume of a substance.

The warm water rises to the surface and cools. Its thermal energy is transferred to the water around it by collision. As the water cools, it becomes denser and sinks. When the water reaches the heater it begins the pattern again. This continuous loop of moving water is called a **convection current**.

Currents of water or air created by the process of convection are called convection currents.

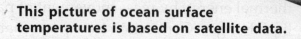

This picture of ocean surface temperatures is based on satellite data.

Convection in Nature

Convection and convection currents send heat around Earth. Convection currents form in Earth's atmosphere and oceans because of uneven heating.

Temperature differences cause convection currents that form huge loops in Earth's oceans. Warm water rises, cools, then sinks. These convection currents deliver heat throughout the oceans. Land and oceans are heated unevenly. This causes the air above them to be heated unevenly, too.

Warm air rises and cools. It becomes cooler and denser and sinks back down to Earth. A convection current has formed.

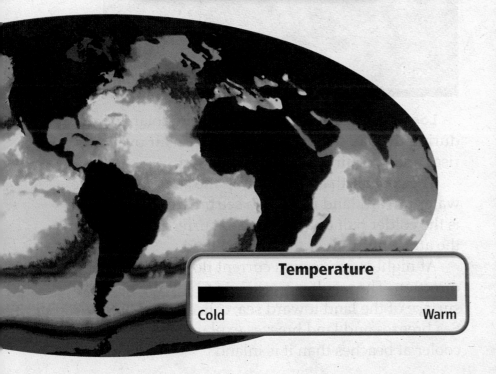

Ocean Surface Temperature

Temperature

Cold   Warm

5. What causes convection currents on Earth?

_____

_____

6. Complete the diagram to compare and contrast convection currents in the atmosphere and in the oceans.

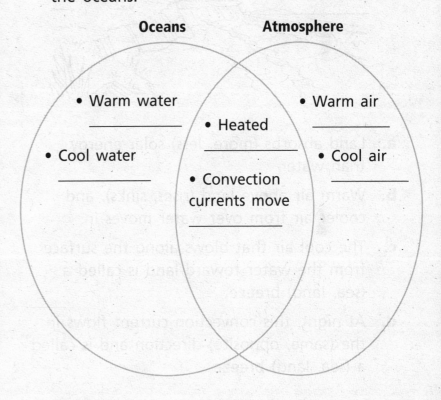

Oceans   Atmosphere

- Warm water
  _____
- Cool water
  _____
- Heated
  _____
- Convection currents move
  _____
- Warm air
  _____
- Cool air
  _____

7. Study the diagram. Underline the correct words in the sentences to describe local winds.

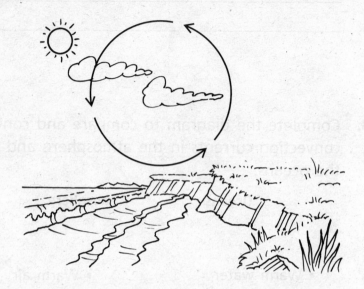

a. Land absorbs (more, less) solar energy than water.

b. Warm air above land (rises, sinks), and cooler air from over water moves in.

c. The cool air that blows along the surface from the water toward land is called a (sea, land) breeze.

d. At night, this convection current flows in the (same, opposite) direction and is called a (sea, land) breeze.

SEA BREEZE Warm air rises over land during the day. Cool air from the ocean moves in and forms a sea breeze.

Warm   Cool

LAND BREEZE Warm air rises over the ocean at night. Cooler air from the land moves in and forms a land breeze.

Cool   Warm

Local Winds The land absorbs more solar energy during the day than water does. Warm air over land rises and cool air over water moves in.

The cool air that blows along the surface from the water toward land is called a **sea breeze**. A sea breeze is the colder half of a convection current that forms in the atmosphere over the sea and land.

At night, a convection current flows in the opposite direction. The result is a cool wind blowing near the surface of the land toward sea, called a **land breeze**. Sea breezes and land breezes explain why the air is cooler at beaches than it is inland.

Temperatures in California

What's the air temperature right now in California? The answer depends on where you are in the state.

In the desert, summer temperatures can get very hot. In the mountains it does not get very warm, and in the winter it may be very cold. Along the Pacific Ocean, temperatures stay even for most of the year.

A location's distance from the equator and from the ocean both affect its temperature.

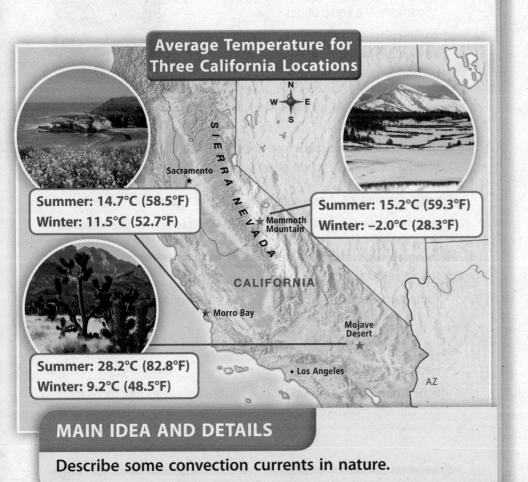

Average Temperature for Three California Locations

Summer: 14.7°C (58.5°F)
Winter: 11.5°C (52.7°F)

Summer: 15.2°C (59.3°F)
Winter: −2.0°C (28.3°F)

Summer: 28.2°C (82.8°F)
Winter: 9.2°C (48.5°F)

Sacramento

SIERRA NEVADA

Mammoth Mountain

CALIFORNIA

Morro Bay

Mojave Desert

Los Angeles

AZ

MAIN IDEA AND DETAILS

Describe some convection currents in nature.

Summary Thermal energy can be transferred by conduction, convection, or radiation. Convection currents play an important role in distributing heat in Earth's atmosphere and oceans.

Find the average summer and winter temperatures for Morrow Bay on the map. Explain why areas near the Pacific Ocean in California have moderate temperatures for most of the year.

_____

_____

_____

_____

Main Idea and Details Describe some convection currents in nature.

_____

_____

_____

Glossary

Draw a picture of a convection current. Label the warm and cool areas of the current. Use arrows to show the direction of flow.

Glossary

atmosphere the blanket of air that surrounds Earth

atmósfera capa de aire y otros gases que rodea la Tierra

conduction the transfer of thermal energy by particle collision

conducción transferencia de energía térmica mediante el choque de partículas

convection (kahn VEHK shuhn) the transfer of thermal energy by the mass movement of particles in a liquid or gas

convección transferencia de energía térmica mediante el movimiento de masa de las partículas que hay en un líquido o gas

convection current a current caused by convection that drives fluid through a circular path

corriente de convección corriente causada por la convección que impulsa los fluidos a través de un recorrido circular

density the amount of mass per unit volume of a substance

densidad cantidad de masa por unidad de volumen de una sustancia

electromagnetic radiation energy transferred by waves that can travel through empty space

radiación electromagnética energía transferida por ondas que puede viajar a través del espacio

electromagnetic spectrum a continuous band that includes all types of electromagnetic radiation

espectro electromagnético banda continua que incluye todos los tipos de radiación electromagnética

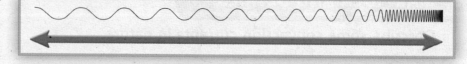

Glossary

greenhouse effect the trapping of heat by certain gases in Earth's atmosphere

efecto invernadero acumulación de calor debida a ciertos gases en la atmósfera terrestre

heat an amount of thermal energy transferred from a hotter object or region to a colder object or region

calor cantidad de energía térmica transferida de un objeto o región más caliente a un objeto o región más frío

land breeze a cool wind blowing near the surface from land toward sea

brisa terral viento frío que sopla cerca de la superficie y va desde la tierra hacia el mar

sea breeze the cool air that blows along the surface from the water toward land

brisa de mar aire frío que sopla sobre la superficie del mar y se dirige a tierra

temperature the average motion energy of particles in matter; a measure of hot or cold

temperatura promedio de la energía cinética de las partículas de la materia; medida de frío o calor

thermal energy the total amount of motion energy from particles in matter

energía térmica cantidad total de energía de las partículas en movimiento de la materia

wave a disturbance that transfers energy from one location to another

onda perturbación que transfiere energía de un lugar a otro

 Visit www.eduplace.com to play puzzles and word games.

Find the English words that are like these Spanish words. List the English words in the chart.

Spanish Word	English Word
atmósfera	
conducción	
convección	
densidad	
temperatura	

Chapter Review

WHAT DID YOU LEARN?

Vocabulary

❶ (Circle) the correct answer on the page.

Comprehension

❷ _____

_____

❸ _____

_____

❹ _____

_____

Critical Thinking

❺ _____

_____

Responding

Think About What You Have Read

Vocabulary

❶ A loop created by warm air rising and cool air sinking is called a / an _____.

A) greenhouse effect

B) electromagnetic wave

C) gamma ray

D) convection current

Comprehension

❷ How does radiation change across the electromagnetic spectrum?

❸ Why do different places on Earth receive different amounts of solar energy?

❹ What are the three ways in which thermal energy is transferred?

Critical Thinking

❺ Explain why rainbows are sometimes seen during or just after a brief rain shower.

WHAT DO YOU KNOW?

How would you describe your weather today?

_____

_____

What kind of severe weather occurs near where you live?

_____

_____

_____

Energy and Weather

Contents

WHAT DO YOU WANT TO KNOW?

Skim the chapter. Read the headings and look at the photos and diagrams. Write one question that you have about each of these topics.

a. Air masses _____

_____

b. Global wind patterns _____

_____

c. California's climates _____

_____

What else do you want to know about energy and weather?

_____

_____

VOCABULARY

air mass a body of air that has similar temperature and water vapor content throughout *(noun)*

air pressure the force exerted by the weight of the air pushing on all surfaces it touches *(noun)*

condensation the change in a substance from a gas to a liquid state *(noun)*

dew point the temperature at which the air is saturated with water vapor *(noun)*

evaporation a process that changes a liquid into a gas *(noun)*

front the boundary between two air masses with different temperature and moisture characteristics *(noun)*

humidity amount of water vapor in the atmosphere at a given time and place *(noun)*

isobar a line drawn on a map to connect points of equal air pressure *(noun)*

precipitation any form of water, including the rain, snow, sleet, and hail, that falls from clouds to Earth's surface *(noun)*

 4.a. Students know that the Sun is Earth's major source of energy. It powers winds, ocean currents, and the water cycle.
4.e. Students know the factors that cause changes in weather.

1 What Causes Weather?

Changes in the weather are caused by differences in air pressure, heat, air movement, and humidity.

Air Pressure

Earth's atmosphere is made up of gases and water vapor. Without the atmosphere, Earth would not have weather.

Air is matter. It has mass and takes up space. Air also has weight. Earth's gravity pulls the molecules of air towards Earth's surface. **Air pressure** is caused by the weight of air pushing on all the surfaces it touches.

Temperature and altitude affect air pressure. The higher the altitude, the less air pressure there is. There is less air pressure in warm air than cold air.

Air pressure is all around. Air pushes on all surfaces it comes into contact with.

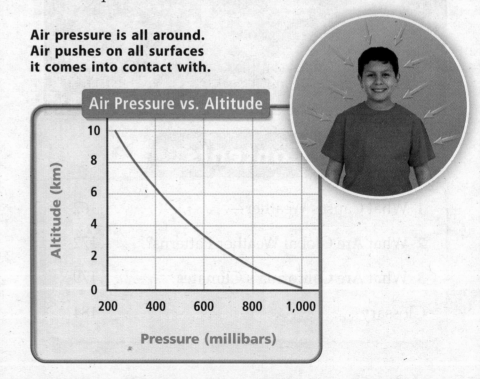

Air Pressure vs. Altitude

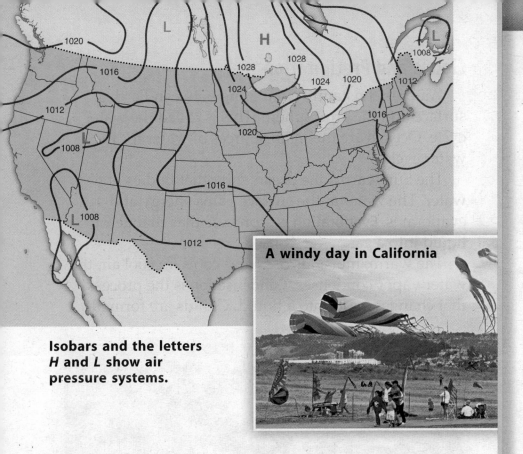

1020 L H 1028 L 1008
1016 1028 1024 1020
1024
1012 1020 1012
1012 L 1016
1020
1008
1016
L 1008
1012

Isobars and the letters *H* and *L* show air pressure systems.

A windy day in California

Winds

Winds form from differences in air pressure. The Sun heats Earth's surface. Air is warm above a warm surface and cold above a cold surface.

Air pressure is different, too. Air pressure is lower above a warm surface than above a cold one. Wind is the movement of air from an area of high pressure to an area of low pressure.

Look at the map above. Centers of high pressure are marked with an *H*. Centers of low pressure are marked with a red *L*. Lines called **isobars** are drawn on the map to connect points with equal air pressure.

1. Look at the graph on page 162. Follow the line with your finger. Where is air pressure highest?

   _____

2. Fill in the blanks to summarize how surface temperature affects the air above it.

	Above a Warm Surface	Above a Cold Surface
Air temperature		
Air pressure		

3. Label an isobar on the map. What is an isobar?

   _____

   _____

4. What are the main sources of water for Earth's water cycle?

_____

5. Look at the photo on this page. Fill in the diagram to summarize what occurred in order for these clouds to form.

> The Sun warms water at the surface. The water _____.

> The warm, moist air rises and cools. The water vapor in the air _____. Clouds form.

> The water droplets in the cloud grow. They fall to the ground as _____.

Clouds and Precipitation

Water is constantly circulating between Earth's surface and the atmosphere. This is called the water cycle. Oceans are the main sources of water for the water cycle.

The Sun warms the ocean and other bodies of water. The water at the surface gains energy and evaporates. **Evaporation** is a process that changes a liquid into a gas.

The warm, moist air rises and cools. In cool air, the water vapor condenses. **Condensation** is the process that changes a gas into a liquid. Clouds are formed.

Water vapor in the atmosphere forms clouds.

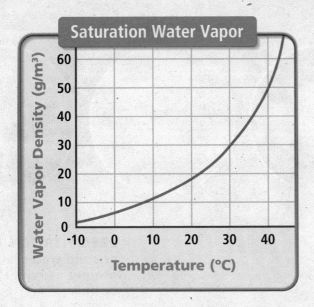

Saturation Water Vapor

Water Vapor Density (g/m³) vs Temperature (°C)

The water droplets in clouds grow and become heavy. Water then falls to the ground as precipitation. **Precipitation** is the rain, snow, sleet, and hail that falls from clouds to Earth's surface.

Humidity

The amount of water vapor in the atmosphere at a given time and place is called **humidity**. Humidity is different from day to day and place to place. Air temperature affects humidity, too.

The temperature at which air is saturated with water vapor is called the **dew point**. Condensation takes place when the air temperature drops below the dew point.

6. Trace the red line on the graph with your finger. What is the water vapor density at the following temperatures?

   a. 10°C _____

   b. 30°C _____

   c. 40°C _____

7. Circle the word that makes each statement about humidity *true*.

   a. Humidity is the amount of water vapor in the (ocean, atmosphere) at a given time and place.

   b. Humidity is (different, the same) every day at every place.

   c. The dew point is the temperature at which air is saturated with (water vapor, precipitation).

   d. (Evaporation, Condensation) occurs when air temperature drops below the dew point.

8. Follow the arrows on the page. Then complete the sequence diagram to tell about Earth's water cycle.

Evaporation

Water changes from a _____ to a _____ called water vapor.

↓

Condensation

Water changes from _____ to tiny droplets of _____.

↓

Precipitation

Liquid or solid water _____ to the ground as rain, _____, snow, or _____.

9. Draw an arrow on the diagram above to show how the water cycle would continue.

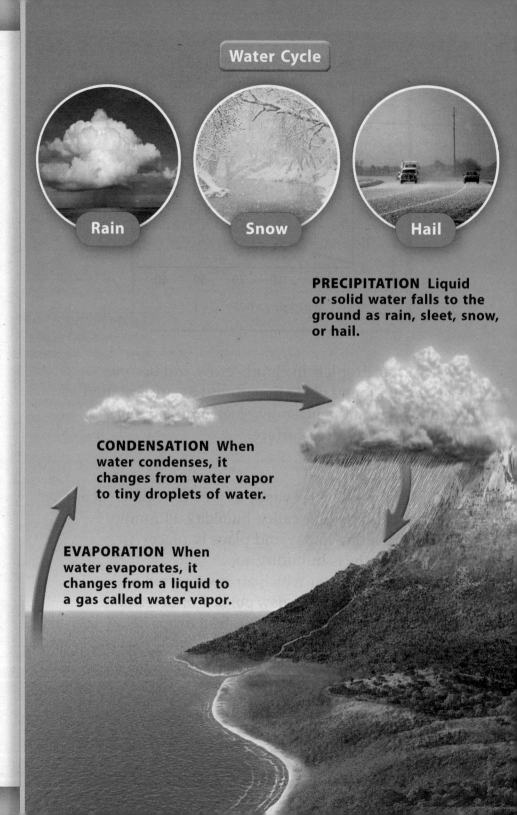

Water Cycle

Rain   Snow   Hail

PRECIPITATION Liquid or solid water falls to the ground as rain, sleet, snow, or hail.

CONDENSATION When water condenses, it changes from water vapor to tiny droplets of water.

EVAPORATION When water evaporates, it changes from a liquid to a gas called water vapor.

Air Masses

Weather changes come from the movement of air masses. An **air mass** is a large body of air that has similar temperature and moisture characteristics throughout. Six major air masses affect North America.

Continental polar air masses are cold and dry. Continental arctic air masses are even colder. They form above the Arctic Circle. These air masses bring cold weather in winter, and cool, dry weather in summer.

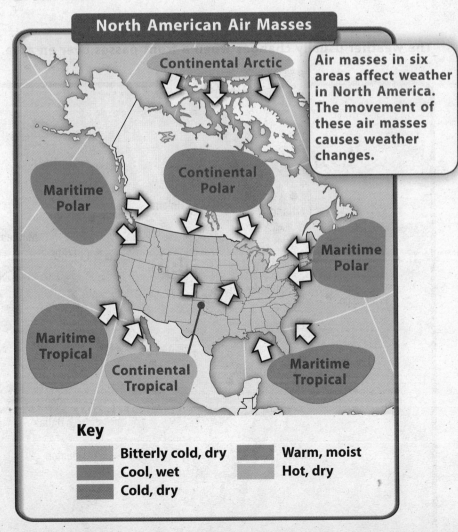

North American Air Masses

Continental Arctic

Air masses in six areas affect weather in North America. The movement of these air masses causes weather changes.

Maritime Polar

Continental Polar

Maritime Polar

Maritime Tropical

Continental Tropical

Maritime Tropical

Key

Bitterly cold, dry	Warm, moist
Cool, wet	Hot, dry
Cold, dry	

10. Study the map. Then list the five North American air masses.

a. _____

b. _____

c. _____

d. _____

e. _____

11. Find California on the map. Which two air masses most affect the weather in California?

_____

I Wonder . . . Air masses take on the characteristics of the region over which they form. Why would a maritime tropical air mass bring hot, humid weather to an area?

_____

_____

_____

_____

12. Complete the chart to tell about three North American air masses.

Weather Condition	Air Mass
• hot and dry • causes droughts	
•	Maritime Polar
•	
• warm and moist • hot, humid weather • heavy rains and thunderstorms	

Continental tropical air masses are hot and dry. These air masses cause droughts if they stay over one area for a long time.

Maritime polar air masses form over oceans. These air masses are cold and moist. They bring strong storms, especially in the winter.

Maritime tropical air masses are warm and moist. These air masses bring hot, humid weather. They can bring heavy rains and thunderstorms.

The weather usually changes when a front passes over an area.

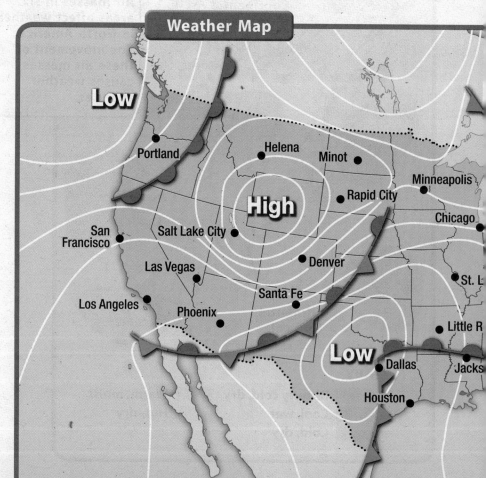

Weather Map

Fronts

A front forms when two air masses meet. A **front** is the boundary between two air masses with different temperature and moisture characteristics. A change in weather usually means a front is moving in.

On a weather map, a cold front is shown by a blue line with triangles. A cold front usually brings stormy weather.

A red line with half-circles marks a warm front. A warm front often brings light, steady rain. A line with both blue triangles and red half-circles marks a stationary front. Along a stationary front the weather is usually cloudy and rainy.

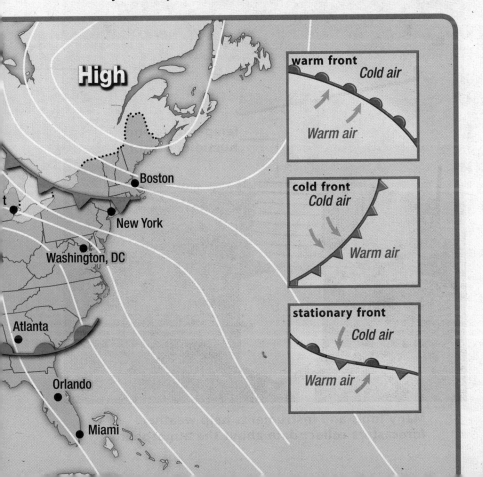

13. A front is the _____ between two air masses with different _____ and _____ characteristics.

14. Look at the weather map.

   a. Find a red line with half-circles. Circle it. What do these symbols represent?

   _____

   b. What type of weather does such a front usually bring?

   _____

   c. Find a blue line with triangles. Put a box around it. What do these symbols represent?

   _____

   d. What type of weather does such a front usually bring?

   _____

15. List two reasons people want to know about the weather.

a. _____

_____

b. _____

_____

16. Complete the table about weather tools.

Weather Tool	Weather Data
	air temperature
hygrometer	
anemometer	
	air pressure
weather balloons	

Tracking Weather

Weather affects people's lives every day. People need to know if storms are approaching. They want to know what to wear or how the weather might affect their activities.

Weather watchers use many tools to gather weather data. Thermometers are used to measure air temperature. Hygrometers measure humidity.

Wind speed is measured with an anemometer (an uh MAHM ih tur). Precipitation is measured with a rain gauge. Air pressure is measured with a barometer.

Many tools and instruments help weather forecasters collect data about the atmosphere.

Pictures taken by satellites help track hurricanes.

Conditions in Earth's atmosphere affect the weather. Weather balloons rise to high altitudes. They take measurements of air pressure, temperature, wind speed, and wind direction in the atmosphere.

Radio transmitters in these balloons send data to a receiver on the ground. Weather satellites send pictures of storms. This information is used by weather forecasters to tell people what the weather will be like.

Weather forecasters also use radar and computer modeling to predict the weather.

MAIN IDEA AND DETAILS

What causes clouds to form?

Summary   Changes in the weather are caused by differences in air pressure, temperature, and humidity. Water moves from Earth's surface to the air and back again in the water cycle. Air masses take on the characteristics of the areas where they form. The movement of these air masses causes weather changes. The boundary where two air masses meet is called a front.

What technology do weather forecasters use to predict the weather?

a. _____

b. _____

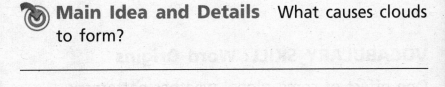 **Main Idea and Details**   What causes clouds to form?

_____

_____

Lesson Preview

VOCABULARY

climate the average weather conditions in an area over a long period of time *(noun)*

Coriolis effect an effect that causes global winds to curve clockwise in the Northern Hemisphere, and counterclockwise in the Southern Hemisphere *(noun)*

jet stream a narrow belt of high-speed winds in the upper troposphere *(noun)*

ocean current a continuous, moving stream of ocean water *(noun)*

VOCABULARY SKILL: Word Origins

One effect of some global weather patterns is drought. The word *drought* is derived from the Old English word *drūgath*, meaning "dryness." Using this information, write your own definition of drought.

_____

_____

_____

4.d. Students know that convection currents distribute heat in the air and oceans.
4.e. Students know the factors that cause changes in weather.

2 What Are Global Weather Patterns?

Air pressure and Earth's rotation affect global weather patterns.

Global Wind Patterns

Winds do not blow in straight lines across Earth. Earth spins on its axis. This causes winds to curve. This effect is called the **Coriolis effect**. It causes winds to curve clockwise in the Northern Hemisphere. In the Southern Hemisphere, winds blow counterclockwise.

Air pressure patterns at Earth's surface cause wind belts. Wind belts are large areas that are usually windy. Wind belts in the Northern Hemisphere are a mirror image of the wind belts in the Southern Hemisphere.

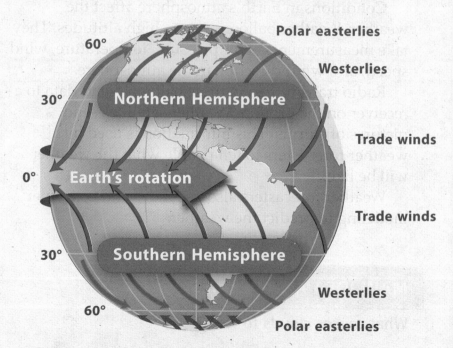

Three major wind belts—the trade winds, the westerlies, and the polar easterlies—move air around Earth.

The area around the equator is called the doldrums. The doldrums is an area of rising air, low air pressure, and very little wind.

Winds blow from areas of high pressure toward areas of low pressure. Look at the map of global winds. Trade winds blow toward the equator from areas of high pressure at 30° north and south latitude. Westerlies blow from west to east between 30° and 60° latitude. Polar easterlies blow from east to west near the poles.

Jet streams are narrow belts of high-speed winds in the upper troposphere. Jet streams can have a "steering" effect on weather.

Jet Streams

This satellite photo shows clouds in the jet stream over the Middle East.

Jet streams are belts of high-speed winds. Jet streams are in the troposphere, the lowest layer of Earth's atmosphere. They do not follow regular paths.

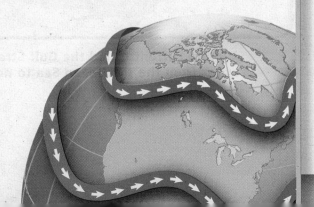

1. Read each clue. Complete the table with the area of Earth or winds that are being described.

Name	Description
	An area of warm, rising air, low pressure, and light winds around the equator
	Winds that blow toward the equator
	Winds that blow from west to east between 30° and 60° latitude
	Winds that blow from east to west near each pole
	Narrow belts of high-speed winds in the upper troposphere

2. Define *ocean current*.

_____

_____

3. Identify two ways in which all the water in an ocean current is alike.

  a. _____

  b. _____

4. Read the information about the Gulf Stream in the caption below the map. The Caribbean Sea is near the Florida coast. Locate this warm water current on the map. Circle it.

Ocean Surface Currents

Oceans affect the lands they border. Areas near the ocean have steady, seasonal temperatures. This is because the temperature of water changes more slowly than the temperature of land. It is also because of ocean currents.

An **ocean current** is a constant, moving stream of ocean water. All the water in a current has similar temperature and density. Ocean surface currents are caused by winds. Currents curve to the right or left depending on what hemisphere they are in.

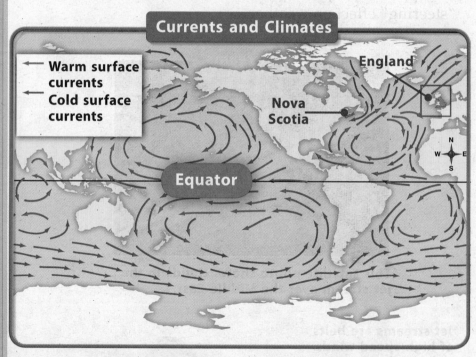

Currents and Climates

← Warm surface currents
← Cold surface currents

England

Nova Scotia

Equator

A warm current called the Gulf Stream brings warm water from the Caribbean Sea to northern Europe.

England

Nova Scotia

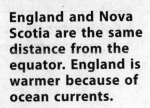

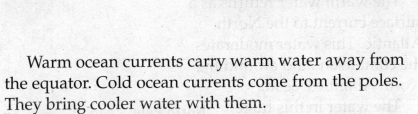

England and Nova Scotia are the same distance from the equator. England is warmer because of ocean currents.

Warm ocean currents carry warm water away from the equator. Cold ocean currents come from the poles. They bring cooler water with them.

Climate describes the average weather conditions in an area over a long period of time. Ocean currents affect the climate. Some places have warmer climates because of ocean currents. Other places have colder climates because of the currents.

5. Read the captions about England and Nova Scotia. Locate these countries on the Currents and Climates map, and notice the type of ocean currents that flow by them. Draw a box around the country with the warmer climate. Why does this country have a warmer climate?

_____

_____

_____

6. Complete the diagram about deep ocean currents.

A deep ocean current starts in the _____
_____ .

⬇

Cold, salty surface water _____, spreads
out, and _____ .

⬇

This deep current flows _____
_____ .

⬇

Some of the water _____ and returns to
the surface. Then it returns as a _____
to the North Atlantic.

Deep Ocean Currents

Deep ocean currents are part of huge convection currents that circle throughout Earth's oceans. Cold water near the poles sinks toward the ocean floor.

Salty water sinks, too. Ice in polar areas is made of fresh water only. When ocean water freezes, the salt is left behind. Water in polar areas is usually both cold and salty.

A deep ocean current starts in the North Atlantic Ocean. Cold, salty surface water sinks. It spreads out and becomes part of a slow-moving convection current.

This deep current flows past the equator into the Southern Hemisphere. Some of the deep waters are warmed here. They rise toward the surface of the ocean.

The warm water returns as a surface current to the North Atlantic. This water moderates the climate on land around the North Atlantic Ocean.

The water in this huge convection current moves in a never-ending cycle. It can take as long as a thousand years for the current to make a single round trip!

Cold water sinks.

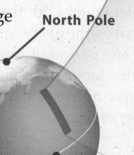

North Pole

Equator

Cold water near the poles is warmed in the ocean near the equator.

Warm water rises.

7. How does the water in this convection current affect the climate of the land around the North Atlantic Ocean?

_____

_____

8. Label the diagram of the deep ocean current. Use these labels:

convection current

very salty water

deep ocean current

surface current

Summary Global weather patterns are influenced by many factors, including air pressure patterns, Earth's rotation, and warm and cold ocean currents.

Complete the table below to summarize the effects of El Niño.

Normal Year	El Niño Year
• Surface winds drive currents _____ to west.	• Surface winds drive currents _____ to east.
• Dry areas stay _____.	• Dry areas become _____.
• Wet areas stay _____.	• Wet areas experience _____.

 Sequence What events signal that an El Niño is going to form?

_____

_____

178

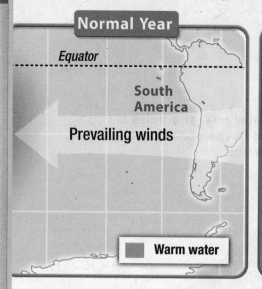
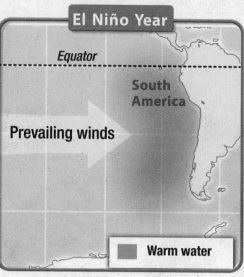

Normally, surface winds near the equator drive currents from east to west.

During an El Niño year, winds blow currents from west to east.

El Niño

In the Pacific Ocean, trade winds usually drive ocean currents from east to west. In some years, the trade winds weaken. They are replaced by winds that blow in the opposite direction. Warm water extends across the Pacific Ocean. This change in wind and current patterns is called El Niño.

Areas that are usually dry might receive heavy rains during an El Niño year. Areas that are normally wet may have droughts. Many people, especially farmers, are affected by El Niño.

SEQUENCE

What events signal that an El Niño is going to form?

What Are California's Climates?

California has four different climate zones.

California Climate Zones

As you have learned, the climate of an area is the long-term average weather conditions. Several factors affect climate. High winds, air pressure systems, and nearby oceans or landforms can all affect climate.

Two main factors are used to describe climate. These are temperature and precipitation. Precipitation is the amount of rain or snow an area gets.

California is divided into four main climate zones. These zones are shown on the map below.

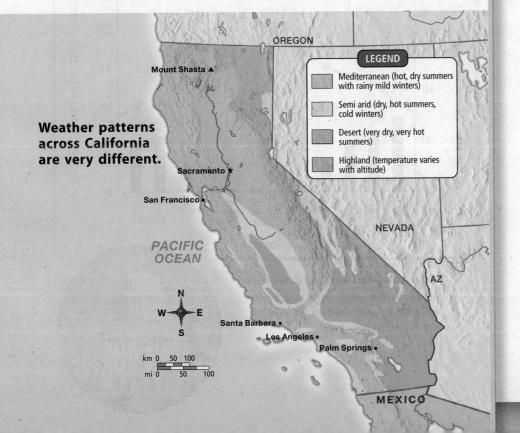

Weather patterns across California are very different.

LEGEND

- Mediterranean (hot, dry summers with rainy mild winters)
- Semi arid (dry, hot summers, cold winters)
- Desert (very dry, very hot summers)
- Highland (temperature varies with altitude)

OREGON

Mount Shasta ▲

Sacramento ★

San Francisco ●

NEVADA

PACIFIC OCEAN

AZ

Santa Barbara ●
Los Angeles ●
Palm Springs ●

km 0 50 100
mi 0 50 100

MEXICO

VOCABULARY SKILL: Word Meaning

Two main factors used to describe climate are temperature and precipitation. *Precipitation* is the amount of rain or snow an area gets. List all the forms of precipitation that you can think of. Circle the ones that occur in your area.

_____

_____

_____

_____

_____

4.e. Students know the factors that cause changes in weather.

179

1. Complete the diagram to tell about Sacramento and its climate.

part of California's _____ Valley

ideal _____ for growing _____

Sacramento

Mediterranean climate: _____ winters and _____ summers

one of the most _____ areas in the world

2. Look at the climate graph. (Circle) the four months in which Sacramento experiences the warmest temperatures.

Sacramento

Sacramento is the capital of California. Sacramento has a Mediterranean climate. This means that it has mild winters and warm, dry summers. Sacramento's pleasant weather makes it one of the nation's fastest growing cities.

The climate of Sacramento is ideal for growing crops. Sacramento is part of California's Central Valley. This is one of the most fertile areas in the world. Crops are shipped from Sacramento to other areas of California and the nation.

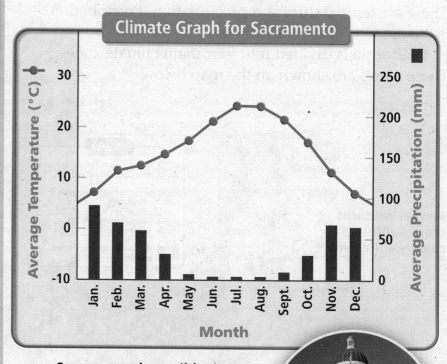

Climate Graph for Sacramento

Average Temperature (°C) / Average Precipitation (mm) / Month

Sacramento has mild winters and warm, dry summers. In which month does the most precipitation fall?

Santa Barbara

Santa Barbara is on the coast of California. Most of California's coastline runs north-south. Santa Barbara is on the section of the coast that runs east-west. The ocean currents that cool the rest of California are not as strong along the east-west coast.

Santa Barbara is near the Santa Ynez Mountains. The mountains provide protection from summer heat. Hot winds can sometimes move down the slopes. These winds increase the risk of wildfires.

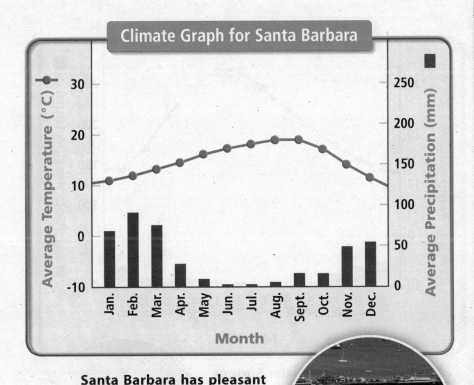

Climate Graph for Santa Barbara

Santa Barbara has pleasant weather all year long.

3. Santa Barbara is located on the part of California's coast that runs _____.

4. Santa Barbara is near the _____ Mountains. These mountains protect Santa Barbara from the _____.

5. Look at the graph. How do the temperatures in Santa Barbara compare with those in Sacramento?

_____

_____

6. Find the month with the highest rainfall. Circle it on the graph.

181

7. Complete the diagram to tell about the climate of Palm Springs.

Cause	Effect
Mountains are located around Palm Springs.	
	The area produces dates, figs, and many other fruits and vegetables.

8. Look at the graph. About how much rain falls in December in Palm Springs?

_____

Palm Springs

Palm Springs lies in the Sonora Desert. The climate is very hot and very dry. The mountains around Palm Springs cause the dry climate. They remove the moisture from winds that blow in from the Pacific.

The land near Palm Springs is good for farming. This area is known for dates, figs, and many other fruits and vegetables.

Palm Springs is a popular resort. It is close to Los Angeles and other cities. And the Sun shines 354 days a year!

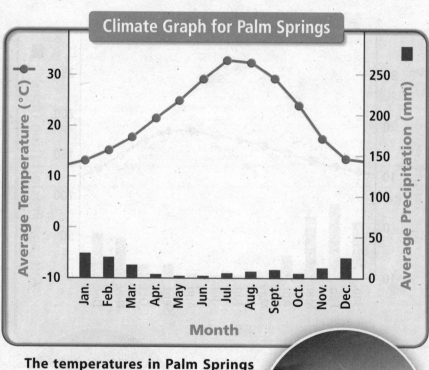

Climate Graph for Palm Springs

The temperatures in Palm Springs are common for desert areas.

Mount Shasta

Mount Shasta is the name of a mountain and a town. Both are in northern California. Northern California has lots of mountains. Its high elevation means lower temperatures. It can also be very rainy.

The area around Mount Shasta has long, warm summers and cold, wet winters. All this water makes northern California a great place for growing trees. Some forest lands are protected. Other forests are used for timber. There are a lot of logging companies in this area of California.

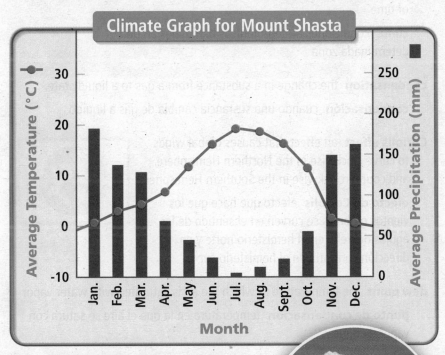

Climate Graph for Mount Shasta

Mount Shasta is one of the tallest mountains in California.

MAIN IDEA AND DETAILS

Describe the climate of northern California.

Summary California has four distinct climate zones based on temperature and precipitation. Fill in the table below to summarize these zones. Use the maps in this lesson to help you.

Climate Zone	Characteristics	City or Landmark
	mild winters; warm, dry summers	
	dry, hot summers; cold winters	areas near Palm Spring
	very dry, hot _____	Palm Springs
Highland	temperatures vary with _____	

Main Idea and Details Describe the climate of northern California.

_____

_____

Glossary

Write a short paragraph, using two words on the page.

_____

_____

_____

_____

_____

Glossary

air mass a body of air that has similar temperature and water vapor content throughout

masa de aire cuerpo de aire cuya temperatura y humedad es prácticamente homogénea

air pressure the force exerted by the weight of the air pushing on all surfaces it touches

presión atmosférica fuerza que ejerce el peso del aire sobre todas las superficies que toca

climate the average weather conditions in an area over a long period of time

clima condiciones meteorológicas habituales en una determinada zona

condensation the change in a substance from a gas to a liquid state

condensación cuando una sustancia cambia de gas a líquido

Coriolis effect an effect that causes global winds to curve clockwise in the Northern Hemisphere, and counterclockwise in the Southern Hemisphere

efecto de Coriolis efecto que hace que los vientos globales se curven en el sentido de las agujas del reloj en el hemisferio norte y en dirección contraria en el hemisferio sur

dew point the temperature at which the air is saturated with water vapor

punto de condensación temperatura en la que el aire se satura con vapor de agua

evaporation (ih vap uh RAY shuhn) a process that changes a liquid into a gas

evaporación proceso en el que un líquido cambia a gas

Glossary

front the boundary between two air masses with different temperature and moisture characteristics

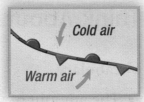

Cold air

Warm air

frente límite entre dos masas de aire que tienen diferentes temperaturas y niveles de humedad

humidity amount of water vapor in the atmosphere at a given time and place

humedad cantidad de vapor de agua que hay en la atmósfera en un momento y lugar determinados

isobar (EYE suh bahr) a line drawn on a map to connect points of equal air pressure

isobara línea dibujada en un mapa para conectar puntos que tienen la misma presión atmosférica

jet stream a narrow belt of high-speed winds in the upper troposphere

corrientes de agua cinturón estrecho de vientos de alta velocidad que hay en la parte superior de la troposfera

ocean current a continuous, moving stream of ocean water

corriente oceánica corriente de agua marina que está en movimiento continuo

precipitation any form of water, including the rain, snow, sleet, and hail, that falls from clouds to Earth's surface

precipitación cualquier forma del agua, lluvia, nieve, granizo y aguanieve, que caen desde las nubes hasta la superficie de la Tierra

Visit www.eduplace.com to play puzzles and word games.

Circle the English words and their meanings for all the glossary words.

Chapter Review

WHAT DID YOU LEARN?

Vocabulary

1 Circle the correct answer on the page.

Comprehension

2 _____

_____

3 _____

_____

4 _____

_____

Critical Thinking

5 _____

_____

_____

Responding

Think About What You Have Read

Vocabulary

1 The amount of water vapor in the air is _____.

A) a front

B) humidity

C) jet stream

D) dew point

Comprehension

2 List three tools that help scientists forecast the weather.

3 What happens to surface water in the North Atlantic Ocean?

4 How would you describe the climate of Sacramento?

Critical Thinking

5 Explain the movement of water in a deep ocean current in terms of convection.

The Biosphere

WHAT DO YOU KNOW?

List one example of each of these topics:

a. Ecosystems _____

_____

_____

b. Biomes _____

_____

_____

c. Biosphere Cycles _____

_____

_____

Contents

WHAT DO YOU WANT TO KNOW?

Skim the photos and headings in this chapter. List one thing you want to find out about each of these topics.

a. Living and nonliving parts of ecosystems

_____

_____

b. Earth's biomes

_____

_____

What else do you want to know about the biosphere?

_____

_____

VOCABULARY

abiotic factor a nonliving part of an ecosystem *(noun)*

biosphere the narrow zone near Earth's surface where life is able to exist *(noun)*

biotic factor a living part of an ecosystem *(noun)*

community the group of living things found in an ecosystem *(noun)*

ecosystem all the living and nonliving things that interact in one place *(noun)*

population all the members of the same type of organism that live in an ecosystem *(noun)*

VOCABULARY SKILL: Word Origins

The prefix *bio-* comes from a Greek word that means "life." One meaning of *sphere* is "the area in which something exists." Use this information to write your own definition of the word *biosphere*.

_____

_____

5.e. Students know that the number and kinds of living things that an ecosystem can support depends on many factors.

1 What Are Ecosystems?

An ecosystem is a community of living things and their surroundings. All of Earth's ecosystems are found in the biosphere. The biosphere is the area where life on Earth exists.

Ecosystems and Communities

Think of the things you might see on the ground in a forest. There could be insects and worms, plants and soil. A section of the forest floor is an example of an ecosystem. An **ecosystem** is made up of all the living and nonliving things that are in one place.

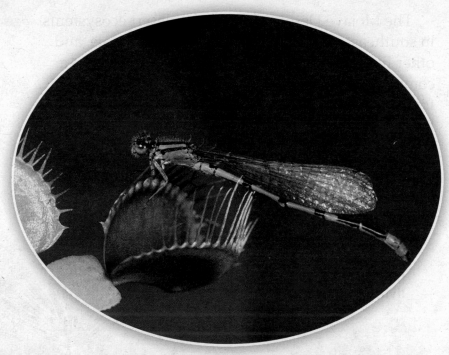

This insect and the plant are biotic factors of an ecosystem.

Ecosystems can be large. A forest or a prairie is an example of an ecosystem. Any living part of an ecosystem is called a **biotic factor**. Biotic factors in a forest could be tiny bacteria or towering trees.

Any nonliving part of an ecosystem is called an **abiotic factor**. Abiotic (ay by AHT ihk) factors include sunlight, soil, water, air, and temperatures.

The **biosphere** (BY uhs feer) is the narrow zone at or near Earth's surface where life is able to exist. It includes the oceans and the lower atmosphere.

1. Fill in the blanks.

   An _____ is a community of living things and their surroundings. It contains all of the living and _____ things that are in one place. The _____ is the narrow zone near Earth's surface where life is able to exist.

2. List all of the living and nonliving things in the photo on page 190. Tell whether each thing is abiotic or biotic.

   a. _____

   b. _____

   c. _____

   d. _____

   e. _____

   f. _____

3. A _____ is all of the living things found in an ecosystem.

4. Use the information in the photo to complete the diagram about the Mojave Desert.

The Ecosystem: _____	
Biotic Factors	**Abiotic Factors**

The Mojave Desert is one of the desert ecosystems in southeastern California. The plants, animals, and other living things of the Mojave Desert make up a community. A **community** is all of the living things found in an ecosystem. They depend on one another for food, shelter, and other needs. They also depend on nonliving things.

Every plant and animal in the desert community is able to live in this dry, hot place.

The Mojave Desert ecosystem includes a community of Joshua trees, bighorn sheep, red-tailed hawks, rattlesnakes, and other living things.

Joshua tree

Populations

Ecology is the study of how plants and animals interact in an ecosystem. Ecologists study populations to understand how an ecosystem works. A **population** consists of all the members of the same type of organism that live in an ecosystem.

The Mojave Desert ecosystem includes populations of Joshua trees and California junipers. Some animal populations are rattlesnakes, bighorn sheep, and jackrabbits. The birth or death of one plant or animal does not change the Mojave Desert very much. But if a population is wiped out, it can affect the whole community.

Bighorn sheep

Red-tailed hawk

Rattlesnake

5. A _____ consists of all the members of the same type of organism that live in an ecosystem.

I Wonder . . . The Mojave Desert includes populations of rattlesnakes, bighorn sheep, red-tailed hawks, and jackrabbits. Hawks and rattlesnakes eat the jackrabbits. How might the loss of the jackrabbit population affect the hawks and rattlesnakes in the area?

_____

_____

_____

_____

Summary An ecosystem is a community of living organisms and their environment. The biosphere includes all of Earth's ecosystems, which are found in a narrow zone at or near Earth's surface. Ecosystems can be very fragile. Tell what might happen if all of the smallest fish in the ocean were to die.

_____

_____

_____

_____

 Main Idea Give examples of the parts of an ecosystem.

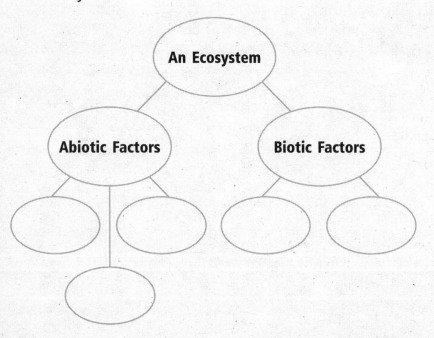

Small fish eat algae and other plants. Larger fish eat the small fish. Feeding relationships such as these are part of all ecosystems.

Desert ecosystems are fragile. This means they are easily thrown out of balance. If humans cut down a lot of desert plants, the animals that depend on those plants would not survive.

In every ecosystem, some species are very important for the whole community. In an ocean ecosystem, the smallest fish are the most important. These fish are food for bigger fish. Sharks and killer whales eat the bigger fish. The whole ocean ecosystem needs large numbers of small fish to survive.

MAIN IDEA

Give examples of the parts of an ecosystem.

194

What Are Earth's Biomes? 2

Earth has six large land biomes. The type of ecosystems found in each biome depends on climate.

Earth's Major Biomes

A **biome** (BY ome) is a large region of similar plant life and climate. Climate is the average weather over a long period of time. Study the map below to find the six major land biomes.

The most important factor in a biome is climate. Different biomes have different climates.

Each biome is home to living things that are adapted to live there. An **adaptation** (ad ap TAY shun) is a trait or characteristic that helps an organism survive in its natural environment.

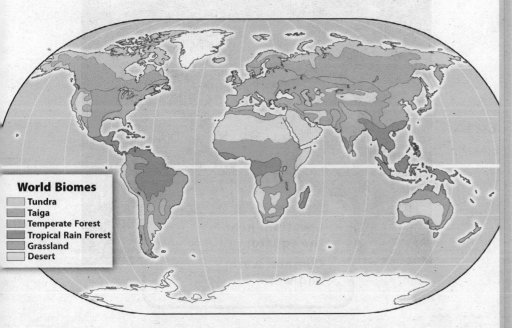

World Biomes
- Tundra
- Taiga
- Temperate Forest
- Tropical Rain Forest
- Grassland
- Desert

Earth is home to six land biomes.

VOCABULARY

adaptation a trait or characteristic that helps an organism survive in its natural environment *(noun)*

biome a large group of ecosystems that have similar characteristics *(noun)*

desert a very dry biome, characterized by sandy or rocky soil and little or no vegetation *(noun)*

grassland a biome characterized by grasses and grasslike vegetation *(noun)*

taiga a forest biome characterized by long, severe winters and short, cool summers *(noun)*

temperate forest a forest biome that experiences four distinct seasons; summer, fall, winter, and spring *(noun)*

tropical rain forest a forested biome, teeming with life, characterized by rainy, hot weather *(noun)*

tundra Earth's coldest biome, with mostly frozen ground *(noun)*

 5.e. Students know that the number and kinds of living things that an ecosystem can support depends on many factors.

195

1. List Earth's six land biomes.

   a. _____

   b. _____

   c. _____

   d. _____

   e. _____

   f. _____

2. Describe a tropical rain forest.

   a. climate: _____

   _____

   b. location: _____

   _____

   c. plant life: _____

   d. animal life: _____

   _____

Tropical Rain Forests and Temperate Forests

There are different types of forest biomes. A **tropical rain forest** is very rainy and hot.

The warm temperatures and heavy rainfall cause life to thrive in a tropical rain forest. There are more kinds of plants and animals in this biome than in any other. The huge number of plants make much of Earth's oxygen. Some of these plants may be used to make new medicines and other useful things people need.

Tropical Rain Forest

Location: near the equator

Climate: warm and wet

Another type of forest biome is called the **temperate forest**. The temperate forest has four seasons: summer, fall, winter, and spring. It does not rain as much in this forest biome as it does in the rainforest.

Animals such as white-tailed deer, rabbits, skunks, and black bears live in temperate forests. Some trees that grow here are maples, oaks, and beeches. These trees lose their leaves in the fall. The fallen leaves add nutrients to the soil in a temperate forest.

Temperate Forest

Location: eastern North America and other places

Climate: four distinct seasons

3. Describe a temperate forest.

   a. climate: _____
   _____

   b. location: _____
   _____

   c. plant life: _____
   _____

   d. animal life: _____
   _____

4. Compare and contrast a tropical rain forest and a temperate forest.

Tropical Rain Forest   **Temperate Forest**

trees   four seasons

near Equator

197

5. Fill in the blanks.

_____ cover the ground in the grasslands biome. There are only a few

_____, and these grow near

_____ and streams.

6. List two types of grasslands.

a. _____

b. _____

7. Complete the chart about grasslands.

Biome	Climate
Grasslands	prairie: savannah: both:

Grasslands and Deserts

Grasses cover the ground in the **grasslands** biome. There are only a few trees in this biome. They grow near rivers and streams.

There are two main grasslands. They are prairies and savannahs. Prairies are found in the central United States. They can be very cold in winter but hot in summer.

Savannahs are found in warmer areas such as central Africa. Most savannahs are hot and dry. This is why few trees grow in savannahs.

Grasslands

Location: central Africa, central U.S., and other regions

Climate: distinct dry season

The **desert** is the driest biome. Most deserts get less than 25 cm (10 in.) of rain in a year. Some deserts may go 20 years without a trace of rain.

Desert plants and animals are adapted to live with little water. Cacti and sagebrush are some plants of the desert. Cacti have leaves with a waxy coating that help the plant lose less water.

There are few living things in Earth's driest deserts. These deserts are filled with sandy dunes that seem to go on forever.

Desert

Location: varies
Climate: extremely dry

8. What is the driest biome?

_____

9. How are organisms adapted to live in a desert environment?

_____

_____

10. Draw a grassland and a desert. Label your pictures.

11. How is the taiga different from the temperate forest?

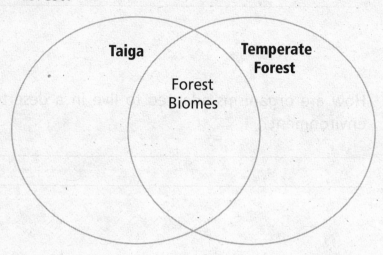

I **Wonder . . .** The taiga is located in northern North America. It has long, harsh winters and short, cool summers. How do trees survive in such a climate?

_____

_____

_____

Taiga and Tundra

The **taiga** is another forest biome. It has long, harsh winters and short, cool summers. The taiga does not get much rainfall. Most of the precipitation in the taiga falls as snow.

The trees in the taiga forest are pines, firs, and spruces. These trees have thin, waxy needles that help them lose less water. Moose, deer, and wolves are some of the animals that live in taiga forests.

Taiga

Location: northern North America and Eurasia

Climate: severe winters and short cool summers

The **tundra** is Earth's coldest biome. The ground is frozen for hundreds of meters down. The lower layers stay frozen all year long. This frozen ground is called permafrost.

Summer is not very warm in the tundra. But the upper layer of ground thaws and the tundra becomes swampy. Mosses, grasses, and other small plants grow, and billions of mosquitoes thrive during the short summer.

Other animals of the tundra are polar bears, wolves, and reindeer. These animals have adapted to survive the extremely harsh weather.

Tundra

Location: near the Arctic Circle

Climate: extremely cold

12. What is Earth's coldest biome?

_____

13. Identify two of each type of organism that lives in the tundra.

a. plants: _____

_____

b. animals: _____

_____

14. Complete the chart about taiga and the tundra.

Biome	Climate
Taiga	severe _____
	short, cool _____
Tundra	extremely _____ winters

Summary Earth has six large land biomes. The climate of each determines the type of ecosystems found in that biome. The ocean biome contains three different zones. Describe these zones in the chart.

Ocean Biome		
Zone		
Location	near shore	beyond intertidal zone	open sea
Life Forms Found There	adapted to _____ _____	tiny _____, crabs, shrimp, and many _____	most life in the _____ layer; some living things _____ to cold, dark water of the deepest part

The types of living things found in each part of the ocean depend on the sunlight.

Ocean Biome

There are three different zones, or areas, in the ocean biome. The intertidal zone is closest to land. The living things in this zone are adapted to crashing waves.

The next zone is the neritic zone. The waters here are usually shallow. Tiny plants, crabs, shrimp, and many fish live in this zone.

The open sea is called the oceanic zone. Its top layer gets the most sunlight and contains the most life. The deepest parts get very little sunlight. Some living things in this zone are adapted to cold, dark water.

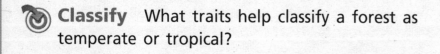 **Classify** What traits help classify a forest as temperate or tropical?

_____

_____

CLASSIFY

What traits help classify a forest as temperate or tropical?

What Cycles Through the Biosphere?

3

Oxygen, carbon dioxide, nitrogen, and water cycle through the biosphere. They are used again and again by living things.

Photosynthesis and Respiration

Algae and plants make the oxygen that is found in the atmosphere. Plants make oxygen and food through photosynthesis. In **photosynthesis**, plants use energy from the Sun to change carbon dioxide and water into glucose and oxygen.

Glucose is a simple sugar that is stored in plants' cells. It is the food and energy plants need. It also is food for animals that eat the plants, and then for animals that eat other animals. The oxygen goes out into the atmosphere.

Plants make oxygen during photosynthesis. People and other animals make carbon dioxide during respiration.

Carbon Dioxide

Photosynthesis

Respiration

Oxygen

VOCABULARY

nitrogen fixation the process of changing nitrogen gas into usable nitrogen compounds *(noun)*

photosynthesis a process during which plants use energy from the Sun to change carbon dioxide and water into glucose and oxygen *(noun)*

respiration the process in which organisms obtain the energy stored in glucose by causing it to react with oxygen *(noun)*

transpiration the process through which water evaporates from plant leaves *(noun)*

VOCABULARY SKILL: Word Origins

The word *photosynthesis* is the combination of the Greek word *phos*, which means "light," and *synthesis*, which means "put together." Therefore, the word *photosynthesis* means "putting together with light." Write the word *photosynthesis* in a sentence.

_____

_____

 5.a. Students know that energy from the Sun is the basis of most food chains and webs
5.b. Students know that energy moves from one living thing to another and between living things and the environment.

203

1. Draw lines from same terms in each process.

Photosynthesis

carbon dioxide + water ⟶ glucose + oxygen

Respiration

glucose + oxygen ⟶ carbon dioxide + water

2. Explain why these processes, although they use the same materials, are opposites.

_____

_____

_____

Most living things use the energy in food through cell respiration. **Respiration** is the process in which organisms obtain the energy stored in glucose by causing it to react with oxygen. Water and carbon dioxide are released through this process.

Both plants and animals perform respiration. Respiration is why oxygen is so important to all life on Earth.

Respiration and photosynthesis are opposite processes. The oxygen made in photosynthesis is used in respiration. The carbon dioxide made in respiration is used for photosynthesis. Oxygen and carbon dioxide keep circling through the biosphere.

Photosynthesis and respiration take place in this kelp forest off the California coast.

The Carbon Cycle and the Oxygen Cycle

The Carbon Cycle Carbon is a basic part of all living things. Carbon moves through the carbon cycle mostly as carbon dioxide gas.

Plants need carbon dioxide for photosynthesis. People and animals eat the glucose in plants. The carbon returns to the atmosphere as carbon dioxide through respiration.

Carbon also moves through the cycle in other ways. When a living thing dies, it decomposes, or breaks down. This process returns carbon to the atmosphere. Burning fossil fuels also releases stored carbon into the atmosphere as carbon dioxide.

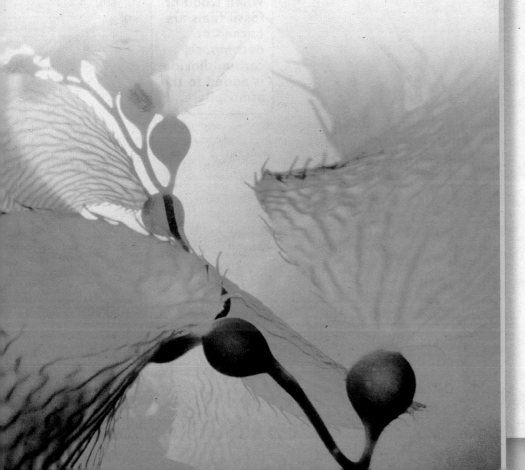

3. In what form does carbon usually move through the carbon cycle?

   _____

4. How do plants and animals add or remove carbon from the atmosphere?

   _____

   _____

5. List two more sources of carbon for the carbon cycle.

   a. _____

   b. _____

6. What are two sources of oxygen in the environment?

_____

_____

7. What links the oxygen and carbon cycles?

_____

_____

I Wonder . . . I have heard of global warming. How does carbon dioxide affect Earth's surface temperature?

_____

_____

_____

The Oxygen Cycle Oxygen also cycles through the environment. Oxygen is released through photosynthesis and when water vapor breaks down chemically.

The oxygen cycle is linked to the carbon cycle. Both oxygen and carbon cycle through living and nonliving things.

Human activity can break these natural cycles. Cutting and burning forests can lead to less oxygen and more carbon dioxide in the environment. Too much carbon dioxide in the atmosphere can cause an increase in global temperatures. This is called global warming.

When wood or fossil fuels are burned or decompose, carbon dioxide is added to the atmosphere.

Key

CO_2 →

O_2 →

The Nitrogen Cycle

Earth's atmosphere contains nitrogen gas. Plants and animals need nitrogen to make proteins and other important compounds. But most living things cannot use nitrogen gas. The nitrogen must somehow be changed into nitrogen compounds. Living things need the nitrogen compounds.

The process of changing nitrogen gas into nitrogen compounds is called **nitrogen fixation**.

Carbon Dioxide and Oxygen Cycle

Both carbon dioxide and oxygen cycle between the air, the ground, and living things.

8. Why is nitrogen important to plants and animals?

_____

_____

9. The process of changing nitrogen gas into nitrogen compounds is called _____.

207

10. List some ways in which nitrogen fixation occurs. (Circle) the method that is used the most.

a. _____

b. _____

I Wonder . . . Nitrogen makes up most of Earth's atmosphere, but most living things cannot use it without nitrogen fixation. Which parts of the natural environment carry out nitrogen fixation?

_____

_____

_____

Nitrogen can be made into fertilizer. Most farms today use fertilizer on the soil.

Nitrogen-fixing bacteria form a close relationship with plants, such as peanuts.

Lightning causes some nitrogen fixation. The energy released by lightning causes nitrogen and oxygen to mix in the air. This forms nitrogen compounds.

Most nitrogen fixation is caused by the action of special bacteria. Some of the bacteria live in soil or water. The bacteria are attached to plant roots. They make nitrogen compounds as the plant grows.

Nitrogen compounds return to the soil. Dead plants and animals decompose. Bacteria breaks down animal waste. Nitrogen is returned to the soil in this way.

Plants reuse the nitrogen compounds in the soil. Nitrogen compounds are changed into the nitrogen gas found in the air.

Human activities can change the nitrogen cycle. Erosion can also wash nitrogen compounds out of the soil. One way of returning nitrogen to the soil is to use fertilizer.

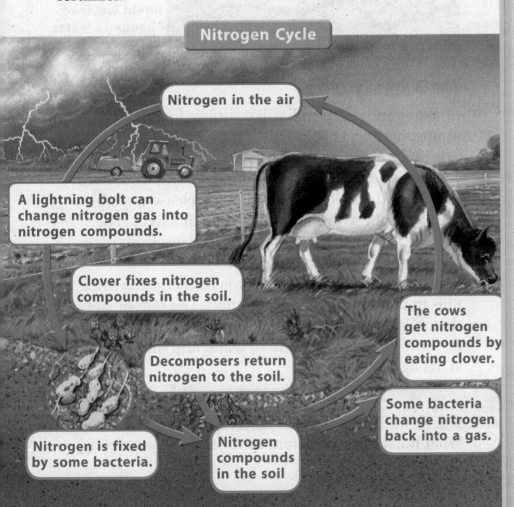

Nitrogen Cycle

Nitrogen in the air

A lightning bolt can change nitrogen gas into nitrogen compounds.

Clover fixes nitrogen compounds in the soil.

The cows get nitrogen compounds by eating clover.

Decomposers return nitrogen to the soil.

Some bacteria change nitrogen back into a gas.

Nitrogen is fixed by some bacteria.

Nitrogen compounds in the soil

11. Fill in the blanks to summarize the nitrogen cycle.

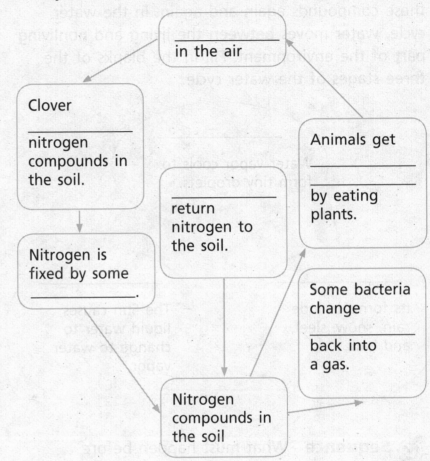

_____ in the air

Clover _____ nitrogen compounds in the soil.

Nitrogen is fixed by some _____.

_____ return nitrogen to the soil.

Animals get _____ by eating plants.

Some bacteria change _____ back into a gas.

Nitrogen compounds in the soil

209

Summary Oxygen, carbon dioxide, nitrogen, and water cycle through the biosphere. Organisms use these compounds again and again. In the water cycle, water moves between the living and nonliving part of the environment. Fill in the blanks of the three stages of the water cycle.

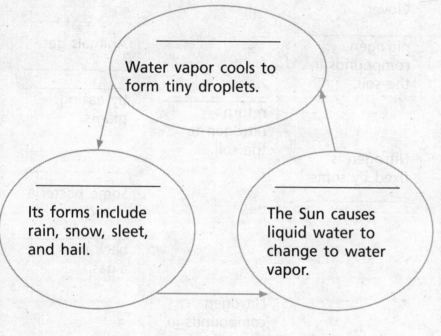

Water vapor cools to form tiny droplets.

_____

Its forms include rain, snow, sleet, and hail.

_____

The Sun causes liquid water to change to water vapor.

Sequence What must happen before nitrogen can be used by most organisms?

_____

_____

210

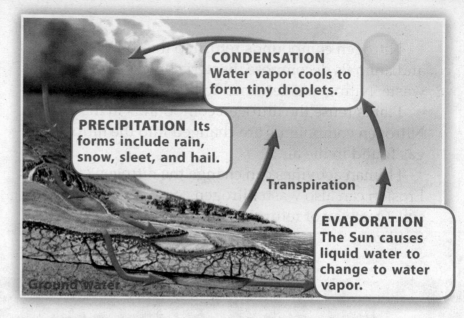

CONDENSATION Water vapor cools to form tiny droplets.

PRECIPITATION Its forms include rain, snow, sleet, and hail.

Transpiration

EVAPORATION The Sun causes liquid water to change to water vapor.

Ground water

The Water Cycle

Water moves from Earth's surface to the atmosphere and back. This is called the water cycle. The Sun powers the water cycle.

The Sun heats water and it evaporates from Earth's surface and the oceans. Plants also release water into the atmosphere through holes in their leaves. The process through which water evaporates from plant leaves is known as **transpiration**.

Water vapor cools and clouds form. Later, water falls to the ground as precipitation. The rain or snow that falls on land is taken up by plants. Some rain or snow flows into a body of water and the cycle starts again.

SEQUENCE

What must happen before nitrogen can be used by most organisms?

abiotic factor a nonliving part of an ecosystem

facto abiótico parte sin vida de un ecosistema

adaptation (ad ap TAY shun) a trait or characteristic that helps an organism survive in its natural environment

adaptación rasgo o característica que le sirve a un organismo para sobrevivir en su medio ambiente natural

biome (BY ome) a large group of ecosystems that have similar characteristics

bioma un gran grupo de ecosistemas que tienen características similares

biosphere (BY uhs feer) the narrow zone near Earth's surface where life is able to exist

biosfera zona estrecha cerca de la superficie de la Tierra y en la cual puede existir vida

biotic factor a living part of an ecosystem

factor biótico parte viva de un ecosistema

community all of the living things found in an ecosystem

comunidad grupo de seres vivos que se hallan en un ecosistema

desert a very dry biome, characterized by sandy or rocky soil and little or no vegetation

desierto bioma muy seco, generalmente de suelo arenoso o rocoso y sin vegetación

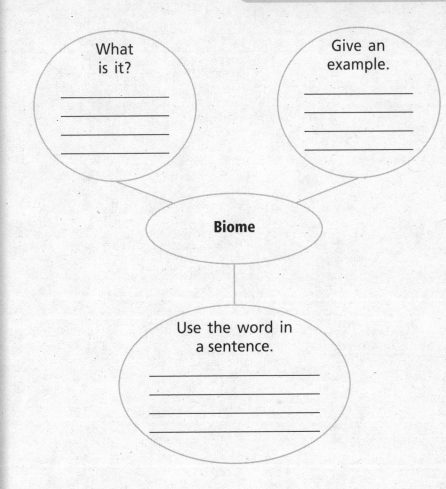

What is it?
_____
_____
_____
_____

Give an example.
_____
_____
_____
_____

Biome

Use the word in a sentence.
_____
_____
_____
_____

(Circle) two words that are opposite processes.

Glossary

ecosystem all the living and nonliving things that interact in one place

ecosistema todos los seres vivos y las cosas sin vida que interactúan en un lugar

grassland a boime characterized by grasses and grass-like vegetation

pastizal bioma caracterizado por hierbas y pastos

nitrogen fixation the process of changing nitrogen gas into usable nitrogen compounds

fijación del nitrógeno proceso que transforma el gas nitrógeno en compuestos útiles de nitrógeno

photosynthesis a process during which plants use energy from the Sun to change carbon dioxide and water into glucose and oxygen

fotosíntesis proceso durante el cual las plantas usan energía del Sol para transformar el dióxido de carbono y el agua en glucosa y oxígeno

population all the members of the same type of organism that live in an ecosystem

población todos los miembros del mismo tipo de organismo que viven en un ecosistema

respiration the process in which organisms obtain the energy stored in glucose by causing it to react with oxygen

respiración proceso mediante el cual los organismos obtienen energía almacenada en la glucosa, haciéndola reaccionar con el oxígeno

Glossary

taiga a forest biome characterized by long, severe winters and short, cool summers

taiga bioma forestal caracterizado por inviernos largos y duros y veranos cortos y frescos

temperate forest a forest biome that experiences four distinct seasons: summer, fall, winter, and spring

bosque templado bioma forestal que tiene cuatro estaciones distintas: verano, otoño, invierno y primavera

transpiration the process through which water evaporates from plant leaves

transpiración proceso mediante el cual el agua se evapora de las hojas de las plantas

tropical rain forest a forested biome, teeming with life, characterized by rainy, hot weather

selva tropical bioma forestal lleno de vida, caracterizado por un clima cálido y lluvioso

tundra Earth's coldest biome, with mostly frozen ground

tundra el bioma más frío de la Tierra, cuyo suelo está en su mayoría congelado

 Visit www.eduplace.com to play puzzles and word games.

Circle the words in this Glossary that are the same in both English and Spanish.

213

Chapter Review

WHAT DID YOU LEARN?

Vocabulary

❶ Circle the correct answer.

Comprehension

❷ _____

_____

❸ intertidal: _____

_____

neritic: _____

_____

ocean zone: _____

_____

_____

❹ _____

_____

Critical Thinking

❺ _____

_____

Responding

Think About What You Have Read

Vocabulary

❶ The driest biome is the _____.

   A) grasslands

   B) taiga

   C) rainforest

   D) desert

Comprehension

❷ What could happen when abiotic factors in an ecosystem change?

❸ What are the characteristics of the three ocean zones?

❹ What substances cycle through the biosphere?

Critical Thinking

❺ Describe what would happen to an ecosystem without green plants.

KWL

WHAT DO YOU KNOW?

List one fact about each of these topics.

a. Food webs _____

_____

_____

b. The energy pyramid _____

_____

_____

c. The role an organism plays in its environment

_____

_____

_____

_____

Roles of Living Things

Contents

WHAT DO YOU WANT TO KNOW?

Skim the pictures and headings in this chapter. List one thing you want to find out about each of these topics.

a. Food webs _____

_____

_____

b. The energy pyramid _____

_____

_____

c. The role an organism plays in its environment

_____

_____

_____

_____

Write one other question you have about the roles of living things.

_____

_____

_____

VOCABULARY

consumer an organism that eats, or consumes, other organisms *(noun)*

decomposer an organism that lives by breaking apart dead organic matter into simpler parts *(noun)*

energy pyramid a pyramid that shows the availability of energy at each trophic level in an ecosystem *(noun)*

food web overlapping food chains in an ecosystem *(noun)*

producer an organism that makes its own food *(noun)*

scavenger an animal that eats the meat of dead animals *(noun)*

trophic level a step in the movement of energy through an ecosystem *(noun)*

VOCABULARY SKILL: Suffixes

In *consumer, decomposer, producer,* and *scavenger* the suffix *-er* has changed verbs to nouns. What does the suffix *-er* mean? Use *consumer* as an example.

_____

_____

5.a. Students know that energy from the Sun is the basis of most food chains and webs.
5.b. Students know that energy moves from one living thing to another and between living things and the environment.

218

1

What Is a Food Web?

Energy moves from producers to consumers in an ecosystem.

Trophic Levels

Food gives energy to living things. Living things that make food are known as autotrophs. They are also called **producers**. Producers include plants, algae, and some bacteria.

A plant uses some of the food it makes. It stores the rest. An animal that eats a plant is fed by this stored energy. The animal uses some of the energy, and stores the rest. When another animal eats the first animal, it gets the stored energy. This is the way energy flows through an ecosystem.

This leaf is a producer. It provides food for the caterpillar.

Each step in the movement of energy is known as a **trophic level**. Producers such as plants are at the lowest trophic level.

Living things in other levels cannot make their own food. They need the producers for energy. These living things are called heterotrophs. They are also called **consumers**. Consumers get energy by eating, or consuming, other living things.

A primary consumer feeds directly on a producer. These consumers make up the second trophic level. A secondary consumer is a living thing that eats the primary consumers. Secondary consumers make up the third trophic level.

This bird is a consumer. It gets its energy by eating food.

1. Compare and contrast producers and consumers.

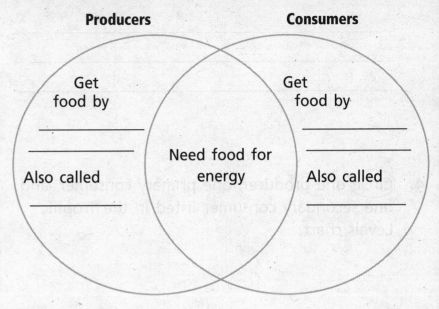

   Producers   Consumers

   Get food by _____   Get food by _____
   _____   _____
   Also called _____   Need food for energy   Also called _____

2. Identify the types of organisms that occupy different trophic levels.

   Third trophic level   Secondary _____

   Second trophic level   Primary _____

   First trophic level   _____

219

3. What is a food chain?

_____

_____

_____

4. Circle one producer, one primary consumer, and one secondary consumer listed in the Trophic Levels chart.

5. How are food chains and food webs related?

_____

_____

_____

Trophic Levels

Secondary Consumers
- Owls
- Wolves
- Snakes

- Sharks
- Dolphins
- Tuna

Primary Consumers
- Squirrels
- Deer
- Seed-eating birds
- Insects

- Herring and other small fish
- Baleen whales

Producers
- Trees
- Ferns
- Mosses

- Algae

A food chain describes the transfer of energy from a producer to a primary consumer to a secondary consumer. Food chains and trophic levels may overlap.

Some animals eat both producers and primary consumers. For example, bears eat fruit and fish. Some of the fish they eat may be secondary consumers that eat other fish.

Overlapping food chains in an ecosystem form a **food web**. Food webs can be on land or in the ocean. Some animals may belong to both a land food web and a water food web.

Scavengers and Decomposers

A **scavenger** is an animal that eats the meat of dead animals. Sometimes once-living things are left to decompose, which means they rot or break down. **Decomposers** live by breaking down once-living matter into simpler parts. Bacteria are Earth's most important decomposers.

Decomposers play a very important role in nature. They return minerals and nutrients to the soil so that new plants can grow. Without decomposers, dead organisms and waste would pile up. The soil would lose nutrients and plants would stop growing. Decomposers are important to keeping the cycle of life moving.

SCAVENGER This raven is a scavenger. It eats the soft parts of dead animals.

DECOMPOSERS Bracket fungus is a decomposer. It can break down a dead tree into smaller parts.

6. Complete the diagram to explain what is likely to happen when a wild animal dies.

_____, such as ravens, eat _____.

↓

_____, such as bacteria, _____ what remains.

↓

Minerals and nutrients _____.

221

7. How is energy used at each level of a food chain or food web?

a. _____

b. _____

8. An energy pyramid shows that more energy is

available at _____ levels than at

_____ levels of an ecosystem.

9. (Circle) the trophic level on the energy pyramid that contains the least amount of energy.

The Energy Pyramid

Food chains and food webs do not show the amount of energy that is passed from one level to the next. Some of the energy is used for living, some is stored, and some is lost as heat. Only the stored energy is passed on to the next living thing.

An **energy pyramid** shows the availability of energy at each trophic level in an ecosystem. More energy is present at lower levels than at higher levels.

Energy that moves through an ecosystem must be renewed. New food energy is always supplied by producers.

Energy Pyramid

Energy	Trophic Level
0.1%	Third-level Consumers
1%	Secondary Consumers
10%	Primary Consumers
100%	Producers

Producers

Primary Consumers

Like cows, people are primary consumers when they eat plants. They are secondary consumers when they eat animals.

The Energy Pyramid and Agriculture

Your food is supplied by agriculture, or farming. You are a primary consumer when you eat plants such as wheat, corn, and rice, or food made from them.

Plants are also fed to chickens, cattle, and hogs. You are a secondary consumer when you eat the animals or food made from animals.

There is less energy available as trophic levels go up. This means that plant energy can supply a lot more food than animal energy. For this reason, raising crops is more energy efficient than raising animals for food.

SEQUENCE

What is transferred along a food chain?

Summary Energy moves in one direction in ecosystems—from producers to consumers. A food web shows how food chains overlap in an ecosystem.

Explain how you can be both a primary and a secondary consumer.

_____

_____

_____

Sequence What is transferred along a food chain?

_____

223

VOCABULARY

carnivore an animal that eats only the meat of other animals *(noun)*

herbivore an animal that eats only plants *(noun)*

niche a species' relationships within the biotic and abiotic factors of its ecosystem *(noun)*

omnivore an animal that eats both plants and other animals *(noun)*

predator an animal that hunts and eats other animals *(noun)*

prey an animal that is hunted and eaten by a predator *(noun)*

VOCABULARY SKILL: Word Roots

Look at the words *carnivore*, *herbivore*, and *omnivore*. The word part *carni-* means *meat*, the word part *herbi-* means *plant*, and the word part *omni-* means *all*. What do you think the word part *vore-* means?

5.c. Students know that populations can be classified by their role in an ecosystem.
5.d. Students know that different kinds of living things may have similar roles in similar biomes.

2 What Roles Do Organisms Play?

Every species in an ecosystem has a niche, or way it fits into an ecosystem.

Niche

Each living thing in an ecosystem has its own niche, or role, in that ecosystem. A species's **niche** is its relationships with the biotic and abiotic factors in the ecosystem. Its niche may include where the species lives and how it raises its young.

A lynx is an example of a predator. The hare that a lynx kills and eats is its prey.

Predator

An animal's niche can also be defined by what it eats and what animals eat it. A **predator** is an animal that hunts and eats other animals.

An animal that is caught and eaten is called the **prey**. Predators and prey are adapted for their niches. A lynx is a predator with good eyesight that can run fast. Its prey is a hare. The hare also runs fast. It may be protected by its fur, which blends into the environment.

Zebras are prey to lions and cheetahs.

Prey

1. Study the pictures. Then complete the chart by giving examples of predators and their prey.

Predators	Prey
lynx	_____
_____	zebra
_____	

2. How are the lynx and the hare adapted to their niches?

a. lynx: _____

_____

b. hare: _____

_____

3. Complete the diagram to compare generalists with specialists.

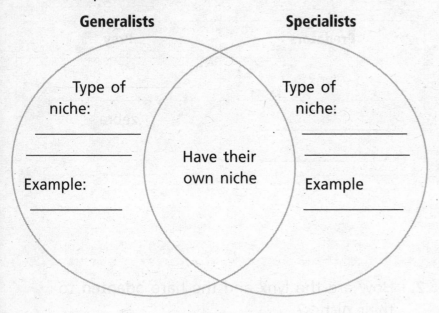

Generalists

Type of niche:

_____

_____

Example:

_____

Have their own niche

Specialists

Type of niche:

_____

_____

Example

_____

4. Circle the four warbler niches in the diagram of the evergreen tree. Where possible, use arrows to show the paths of the warblers as they hunt within their niches.

226

Some species are called generalists. This means they fit into a broad niche. Raccoons are generalists. They eat almost anything: nuts, berries, fish, even garbage!

Other species are called specialists. They have a very small niche. For example, evergreen trees are home to four species of wood warblers. The birds all eat insects, but they hunt in different ways in different parts of the tree.

The warblers also nest and raise their young at different times. This is so that they won't all need food for their young at the same time.

Warbler Niches

CAPE MAY WARBLER This warbler hunts in the top of the tree. It moves up and down.

BLACKBURNIAN WARBLER This warbler also hunts in the top of the tree. It moves from one side of the tree to the other.

BAY BREASTED WARBLER This warbler hunts in the middle of the tree.

YELLOW-RUMPED WARBLER This warbler stays in the bottom part of the tree.

Food Webs

Each ecosystem has a different food web, but all food webs have the same parts. These parts are producers, herbivores, carnivores, omnivores, and decomposers.

Producers are at the bottom of an ecosystem's food webs. Plants and algae are producers. They use the energy of the Sun to make food. This energy is passed to **herbivores** (HUR buh vawrs), which are plant-eating animals. Herbivores are primary consumers.

Herbivore

A jackrabbit is an herbivore, or a plant-eating animal.

5. Identify the parts of a food web.

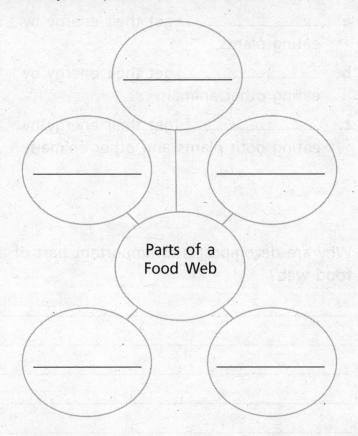

Parts of a Food Web

6. Producers are at the _____ of an ecosystem's food webs. Producers include _____ and _____.

7. What energy source do producers use to make food?

_____

8. Identify the type of consumer.

a. _____ get their energy by eating plants.

b. _____ get their energy by eating other animals.

c. _____ get their energy by eating both plants and other animals.

9. Why are decomposers an important part of a food web?

_____

_____

_____

_____

Animals that eat herbivores are called carnivores. **Carnivores** are also consumers. They get their energy from eating other animals that they hunt.

Omnivores (AHM nuh vawrs) get energy by eating both plants and other animals. Carnivores and omnivores are found at or near the top of a food web.

Decomposers are living things that feed on dead plants and animals, breaking them down into nutrients that go into the soil. The path of nutrients from plants to animals and back to plants takes place in every ecosystem.

Carnivore

A hawk is a carnivore, or a meat-eating animal.

Omnivore

A roadrunner is an omnivore, eating both plants and animals.

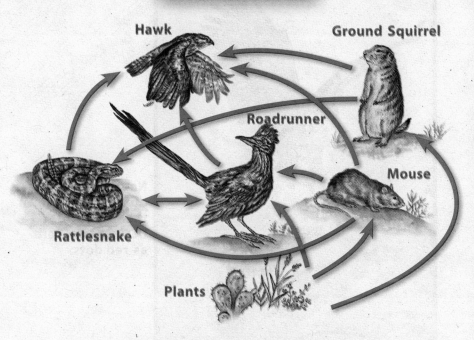

Desert Food Web

Hawk

Ground Squirrel

Roadrunner

Rattlesnake

Mouse

Plants

A food web shows all the feeding relationships in an ecosystem. Find the producers, herbivores, and carnivores shown here. Arrows between animals point from prey to predator.

The desert does not have many species, but it still has a complex food web. Desert producers are the creosote bush, sagebrush, and cactus. Rabbits and mice are herbivores that eat these plants and their seeds.

Rattlesnakes and hawks are carnivores that eat desert herbivores. Roadrunners are omnivores. They eat mostly meat. In the winter when animals are scarce they eat plants.

A top carnivore, such as a hawk or lion, shows that the ecosystem is healthy because there is enough food to support the food web.

10. Trace several different paths from the bottom to the top of the desert food web. Circle the herbivores. Put a box around the carnivores.

I Wonder . . . The presence of a top carnivore shows that an ecosystem is healthy. There is enough food to support the entire food web. What conditions might make an ecosystem unable to support a top carnivore? What do you think?

_____

_____

_____

_____

_____

_____

229

11. Complete the diagram to show how a toxin that cannot be broken down by natural processes could travel up a food chain. Start at the bottom.

> The toxin builds to its highest level at the _____.

↑

> Carnivores eat the _____.
> Toxins continue to concentrate.

↑

> _____ eat the plants. The more plants they eat, the more toxin collects in their bodies.

↑

> Plants absorb the _____.

↑

> The toxin is spilled on the ground.

12. What is this process called?

_____

230

DDT in a Food Chain

Eagle

Big fish

Small fish

Zooplankton

Tiny fish

Natural processes do not break down the insecticide DDT, shown here as red dots.

Biomagnification

Nutrients and energy are passed from one living thing to another in a food chain. Toxins are poisons that may be passed up a food chain, too.

Some toxins are not broken down by natural processes. The toxin stays in the body of the animal that ate the toxin. The toxin is passed up the food chain when this animal is eaten by another animal.

Toxins are in their highest levels at the top of the food chain, in humans and other animals. They get the entire amount of the toxin from all the lower levels. This effect is called biomagnification.

Biologist Rachel Carson was one of the first scientists to observe and describe biomagnification. She showed that DDT, an insecticide, traveled up the food chain. It harmed birds and other animals. The chart on page 230 shows how DDT can travel up an ocean food chain.

Today, large-scale use of DDT is banned worldwide.

Farmers now use pesticides that do not have DDT.

Summary Every species in an ecosystem has a niche that includes the species' relationships with the biotic and abiotic factors in the system.

Explain biomagnification, using DDT as an example.

_____

_____

_____

🎯 **Classify** What are the main parts of every food web?

Main Parts of a Food Web

producers | _____ | _____

_____ | _____

Lesson Preview

VOCABULARY

commensalism a relationship between two species, in which one benefits while the other species is neither harmed nor helped *(noun)*

mutualism a close relationship in which both species benefit *(noun)*

parasitism a relationship between two species, in which one species benefits while the other species is harmed *(noun)*

symbiosis a close living relationship between two species *(noun)*

VOCABULARY SKILL: Word Parts

The suffix *-ism* can mean "a state or quality of." One meaning of the word *mutual* is "shared." Read the definition above. How does the meaning of *mutual* change when *-ism* is added?

_____

_____

5.c. Students know that populations can be classified by their role in an ecosystem.
5.d. Students know that different kinds of living things may have similar roles in similar biomes.

3 What Is Symbiosis?

Symbiosis is a close relationship between two different species. Mutualism, commensalism, and parasitism are all symbiotic relationships.

Mutualism and Commensalism

Three ways living things interact are predation, competition, and symbiosis. Animals eat other animals in predation. Competition takes place when two species try to use the same limited resource, such as a food supply.

In **symbiosis** (sihm bee OH sis), two species have a close living relationship. There are three kinds of symbiotic relationships. They are called mutualism, commensalism, and parasitism.

A lichen is an alga and a fungus living in symbiosis.

The symbiotic relationship is called **mutualism** (MOO choo uh lihz uhm) when two species both benefit from the relationship. One example of this is the relationship between sea anemones (uh NEM uh neez) and clownfish.

Anemones feed on fish. They do not move from place to place. They capture passing fish with their stinging tentacles. Clownfish live among the anemone tentacles. They are immune to the stings. The anemone protects the clownfish from being eaten by other fish. The clownfish cleans the anemone's tentacles.

MUTUALISM The sea anemone's stinging tentacles keep the clownfish's predators away. The clownfish keeps the sea anemone clean.

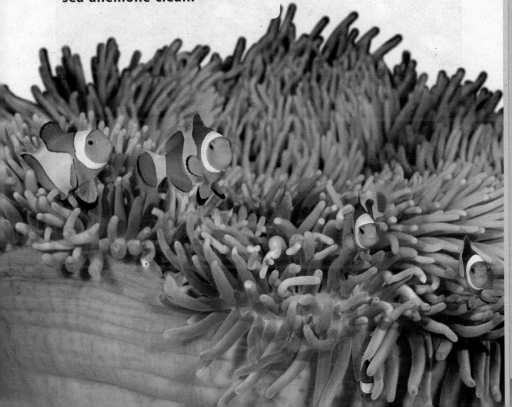

1. In symbiosis, two species have a

_____.

2. Identify the three kinds of symbiotic relationships.

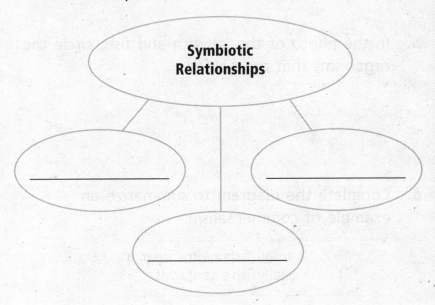

Symbiotic Relationships

3. How does the relationship between a sea anemone and a clownfish benefit both species?

a. The clownfish benefits because _____

_____.

b. The sea anemone benefits because _____

_____.

4. Define commensalism.

_____

_____

5. In the photo of the jellyfish and fish, circle the organisms that are helped.

6. Complete the diagram to summarize an example of commensalism.

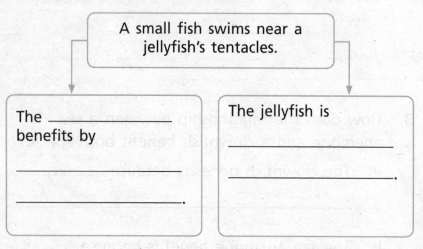

> A small fish swims near a jellyfish's tentacles.

| The _____ benefits by _____ _____. | The jellyfish is _____ _____. |

Commensalism (kuh MEHN suh lihz uhm) is another type of relationship between two species. One species benefits from the relationship. The other is neither harmed nor helped.

A robin building a nest in an oak tree is one example. The robin has a safe place to lay its eggs. The oak tree is neither harmed nor helped.

Commensal relationships are rare. Usually, one species is helped or harmed at least slightly.

COMMENSALISM Small fish hide from predators near the poisonous tentacles of jellyfish. The jellyfish is unaffected by the fish.

Parasitism

Parasitism is a relationship between two species in which one species benefits while the other species is being harmed. The organism causing the harm is called a parasite. The harmed organism is called the host.

Parasites usually weaken their hosts slowly instead of killing them quickly. The parasite has a constant food supply when feeding on the living host.

Leeches, tapeworms, and fleas are common examples of parasites. Their mouths attach to the skin of their host. Most parasites live off the host's blood.

PARASITISM Ticks can transmit disease as they feed on a host.

7. In parasitism, the parasite _____

and the host is _____.

8. Identify some common parasites.

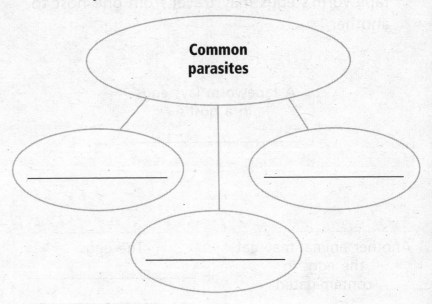

9. What do most parasites live off?

_____

235

10. Where do tapeworms get their food?

_____

11. Complete the diagram to show how a tapeworm's eggs may travel from one host to another.

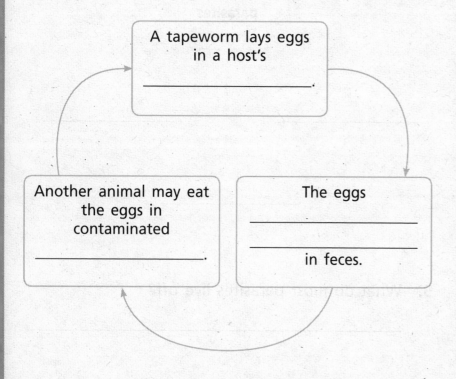

A tapeworm lays eggs in a host's

_____

Another animal may eat the eggs in contaminated

_____ .

The eggs

_____

_____

in feces.

Types of Parasites

Tapeworms are long, flat worms that live in the intestines of dogs, humans, and many other animals. The tapeworm attaches to the inner wall of an animal's intestine. The tapeworm absorbs food in the intestine.

A tapeworm's eggs are laid in the host's intestine. They leave the host's body in feces. Another animal may eat the eggs, usually with contaminated food or water.

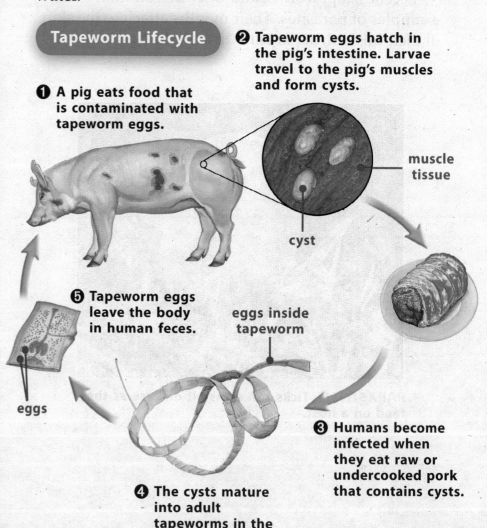

Tapeworm Lifecycle

❶ A pig eats food that is contaminated with tapeworm eggs.

❷ Tapeworm eggs hatch in the pig's intestine. Larvae travel to the pig's muscles and form cysts.

muscle tissue

cyst

❺ Tapeworm eggs leave the body in human feces.

eggs inside tapeworm

eggs

❸ Humans become infected when they eat raw or undercooked pork that contains cysts.

❹ The cysts mature into adult tapeworms in the human intestine.

Mistletoe can weaken or even kill its host tree.

In the second host, the eggs hatch into larvae and travel to muscle cells. There they form cysts. Humans and other animals are infected when they eat meat that has these cysts in it.

Parasites often carry harmful diseases. For example, the deer tick is a parasite of deer, humans, and other animals. It can pass on the bacteria that causes Lyme disease.

Plants and trees can have parasites, too. Plant parasites soak up nutrients from the host. Plant parasites can weaken or kill a plant or tree.

12. Complete the sentences about parasites.

a. The deer tick can carry _____ that cause _____.

b. Plant parasites take _____ from the host. This activity can _____ a plant or tree.

I Wonder . . . Why haven't plant parasites weakened or killed all plants?

_____

_____

_____

_____

Summary Symbiosis is a close living relationship between two species. Define each type of symbiosis.

Mutualism: _____

_____

Commensalism: _____

_____

Parasitism: _____

_____

 Compare and Contrast What are ways that symbiotic relationships help and hurt humans?

| Helpful to humans | | Harmful to humans |

```
  _____     Close       _____
                  relationship
  _____    between      _____
                   humans and
  _____    another      _____
                    species
```

Three Parasites of Humans

Parasite	Description	Treatment
Malaria	Infection with this protist can cause chills, fever, diarrhea, and death.	Antimalarial drugs
Scabies	Scabies are small mites that burrow under the skin of the host, forming tiny tunnels and causing an itchy rash.	Prescription medication
Lice	Head lice live on the human scalp, and feed on human blood several times aday, causing intense itching of the scalp.	Combination of special shampoo and egg removal

Symbiosis with Humans

Some organisms living inside you keep you healthy. Large numbers of bacteria live in your large intestine. These bacteria feed on food that has not been fully digested. Some of the bacteria produce vitamin K and other nutrients humans need. This is an example of mutualism. It is good for both species.

Some symbiotic relationships with humans are parasitic. Parasites can cause anything from minor illnesses, such as ringworm, to serious diseases, such as malaria. Malaria kills about 2 million people every year.

COMPARE AND CONTRAST

What are ways that symbiotic relationships help and hurt humans?

carnivore an animal that only eats the meat of other animals

carnívoro animal que se alimenta sólo de la carne de otros animales

commensalism (kuh MEHN suh lihz uhm) a relationship between two species, in which one benefits while the other species is neither harmed nor helped

comensalismo relación entre dos especies, en que una se beneficia y la otra no se ve beneficiada ni perjudicada

consumer An organism that eats, or consumes, other organisms

consumidor organismo que come o consume otros organismos

decomposer an organism that lives by breaking apart dead organic matter into simpler parts

desintegrador organismo que vive de descomponer en partes menos complejas la materia orgánica muerta

energy pyramid a pyramid that shows the availability of energy at each trophic level in an ecosystem

pirámide energética pirámide que muestra la disponibilidad de energía en cada nivel trófico de un ecosistema

Look through the glossary. List the words that describe living things by the way they obtain energy.

_____

_____

_____

_____

_____

Look through the glossary. (Circle) the words that describe types of symbiosis.

food web overlapping food chains in an ecosystem

red alimenticia cadenas alimenticias que se superponen en un ecosistema

herbivore (HUR buh vawr) an animal that eats only plants

herbívoro animal que se alimenta sólo de plantas

mutualism (MYOO choo uh lihz uhm) a close relationship in which both species benefit

mutualismo relación de la que dos especies salen beneficiadas

niche a species' relationships with the biotic and abiotic factors of its ecosystem

nicho relación de una especie con los factores bióticos y abióticos de su ecosistema

omnivore (AHM nuh vawr) an animal that eats both plants and other animals

omnívoro animal que se alimenta de plantas y de otros animales

parasitism a relationship between two species, in which one species benefits while the other species is harmed

parasitismo relación entre dos especies, en la que una se beneficia mientras que la otra sale perjudicada

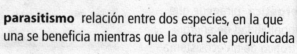

Glossary

predator an animal that hunts and eats other animals

depredador animal que caza y se alimenta de otros animales

predator

prey

prey an animal that is hunted and eaten by a predator

presa animal al que un depredador caza y del cual se alimenta

producer an organism that makes its own food

productor organismo que produce su propia comida

scavenger an animal that eats the meat of dead animals

carroñero animal que se alimenta de la carne de animales muertos

symbiosis (sihm bee OH sis) a close living relationship between two species

simbiosis estrecha relación entre dos especies que viven juntas

trophic level a step in the movement of energy through an ecosystem

nivel trófico fase del movimiento de energía a través de un ecosistema

 Visit www.eduplace.com to play puzzles and word games.

Find the Spanish words that are like these English words. List the Spanish words in the chart.

English Word	Spanish Word
niche	
parasitism	

241

Chapter Review

WHAT DID YOU LEARN?

Vocabulary

❶ (Circle) the correct answer on the page.

Comprehension

❷ _____
_____

❸ _____
_____

❹ _____
_____

Critical Thinking

❺ _____
_____
_____
_____
_____

Responding

Think About What You Have Read

Vocabulary

❶ A producer is on an ecosystem's lowest _____.

A) trophic level

B) energy pyramid

C) food web

D) niche

Comprehension

❷ Explain how energy is transferred when one living thing eats another.

❸ Which animals in a food web are most affected by biomagnification?

❹ How do parasitism and predation differ?

Critical Thinking

❺ A disease kills all the herbivores and omnivores in an ecosystem. Can the ecosystem survive with only producers and carnivores? Explain your answer.

Populations

WHAT DO YOU KNOW?

List one fact about each of the following topics.

a. Limits on population growth _____

_____

b. How environments change _____

_____

c. How human activity affects ecosystems _____

_____

Contents

WHAT DO YOU WANT TO KNOW?
Look at the pictures and headings in this chapter. List one thing you want to find out about each of these topics.

a. Limits on population growth _____

_____

b. Ecological succession _____

_____

c. How human activity affects ecosystems _____

_____

Write one other question you have about populations.

_____

_____

_____

VOCABULARY

competition the struggle among living things to use the same resources in an ecosystem *(noun)*

disease a condition that prevents an organism from functioning properly *(noun)*

endangered species a species that is close to becoming extinct *(noun)*

extinction the complete disappearance of a species *(noun)*

invasive species plants or animals that are not native to an ecosystem *(noun)*

limiting factor something that restricts the growth and distribution of a population *(noun)*

predation when one organism—the predator—catches and feeds on another organism—the prey *(noun)*

threatened species a species that is close to becoming endangered *(noun)*

1 What Limits Population Growth?

Population size depends on resources, predator-prey relationships, diseases, and competition.

Limited Resources

The watering hole shown in the picture below is drying up. There is not enough water for all the animals.

A lack of water can be a limiting factor to the animals in an ecosystem. A **limiting factor** is something that restricts the growth and distribution of a population. All populations have limiting factors.

Some limiting factors are food, water, and space. They can also involve competition, predation, disease, invasive species, and human activities.

A lack of water can be a limiting factor to the elephant and lion populations.

Competition

Competition is a limiting factor. **Competition** is the struggle among living things to use the same resources in an ecosystem.

Sometimes competition takes place between members of the same species. Two robins may compete for the best place to build a nest. Sometimes competition takes place between different species. Owls and hawks hunt for the same type of food.

People compete with plants and animals for resources, too. To meet their own needs, people sometimes destroy plant and animal habitats.

Resource Competition

RAIN FOREST Plenty of water and warm temperatures support many plant and animal populations in the rain forest.

DESERT The lack of water in the desert leads to small plant and animal populations.

1. List three limiting factors in an ecosystem.

   a. _____

   b. _____

   c. _____

2. Why does competition exist in an ecosystem?

   _____

   _____

   _____

   _____

3. Look at the photo on this page. What might be a limiting factor on this population of walruses? Explain your choice.

_____

_____

_____

4. Complete the diagram to tell about an ecosystem's carrying capacity.

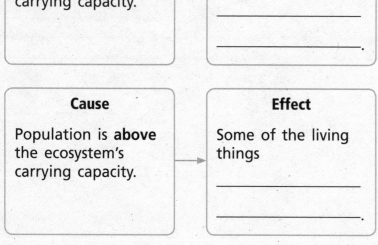

Cause		Effect
Population is **below** the ecosystem's carrying capacity.	→	Population grows until _____ _____.

Cause		Effect
Population is **above** the ecosystem's carrying capacity.	→	Some of the living things _____ _____.

248

Ecosystem Balance

The number of living things an ecosystem can support is determined by limiting factors. This number is called the carrying capacity of the ecosystem. The ecosystem is in balance when the carrying capacity for all species has been reached.

Populations can grow above the carrying capacity, but only for a short time. The resources cannot support a population that has grown larger than the carrying capacity. Some of the living things will leave the area or die.

If the population is below the carrying capacity, it will grow until some factor limits it.

Although it looks crowded, this ecosystem can support all these walruses.

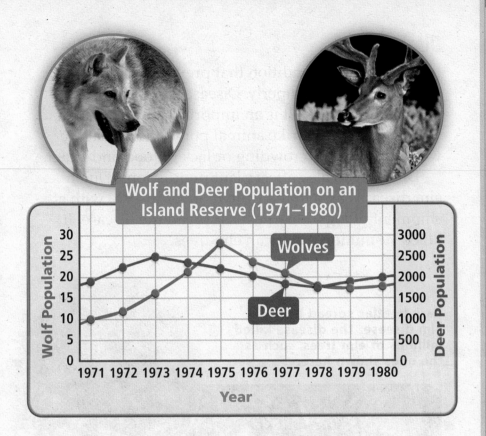

Wolf and Deer Population on an Island Reserve (1971–1980)

Wolves

Deer

Wolf Population: 30 25 20 15 10 5 0

Deer Population: 3000 2500 2000 1500 1000 500 0

Year: 1971 1972 1973 1974 1975 1976 1977 1978 1979 1980

Predators

Predation takes places when one animal—the predator—catches and feeds on another animal—the prey.

Predation is another limiting factor in an ecosystem. The graph above shows the populations of predators (wolves) and their prey (deer) in an ecosystem. The high points show when populations are largest. The low points show when populations are smallest.

Notice that the high points and low points for both animals follow the same pattern. The numbers for predators and prey usually cycle from high to low in a natural process of population control.

5. Analyze the graph.

a. (Circle) the year on the *x*-axis when the deer population was at its greatest.

b. How many deer were living on the island when their population was at its greatest? (Circle) that number on the right *y*-axis.

c. (Circle) the year on the *x*-axis when the wolf population was at its greatest.

d. How many wolves were living on the island when their population was at its greatest?

_____

6. What is the limiting factor for the deer population in this ecosystem?

_____

7. What is the carrying capacity for deer on this island? Explain your answer.

_____
_____
_____
_____

249

_____

_____

_____

_____

_____

Diseases

A **disease** is a condition that prevents a living thing from functioning properly. Disease can stop population growth. It is an important limiting factor.

Diseases often strike animal populations that are weakened by overcrowding or lack of food and water.

Disease can also affect plant populations. Dutch elm disease came to the United States in 1930 with a shipment of logs. Bark beetles spread the disease. It killed 77 million American elm trees.

Bark beetles spread Dutch elm disease. The disease killed millions of elm trees, such as the ones shown here.

This Chinese snakehead is an invasive species. It competes with native species in lakes and streams in North America.

Invasive Species

The natural balance of an ecosystem can be changed when a living thing arrives from another place. **Invasive species** are plants or animals that are not native to an ecosystem.

The Chinese snakehead, shown above, is an invasive species in North America. It was imported from Asia for aquariums and for food. Some of the snakeheads escaped and entered freshwater lakes and streams in North America.

Invasive species harm ecosystems because they have no natural predators. Their populations can grow quickly. They can destroy habitats and disturb food chains.

8. What is an invasive species?

   _____

   _____

9. Complete the diagram to tell about invasive species.

   They can destroy
   _____.

   They can as
   _____
   food chains.

   Invasive species can harm ecosystems.

   They have no natural
   _____.

   Their populations can grow
   _____.

10. List three causes for extinction.

a. _____

b. _____

c. _____

11. Complete the diagram.

> A threatened species is one that is
> _____ .

↓

> An endangered species is one that is
> _____ .

↓

> An extinct species is one that has
> _____ .

Extinction

Most of the species that ever lived on Earth are now extinct. **Extinction** is the complete disappearance of a species. Extinction can happen when an ecosystem changes. A species unable to survive in its ecosystem becomes extinct.

Invasive species can cause extinction. Some species become extinct naturally. Others become extinct because of the actions of humans.

Humans increase the rate of extinction by habitat destruction. When people build homes, roads, and businesses, they destroy natural ecosystems. Living things lose the resources they need when habitats are destroyed.

Passenger pigeons became extinct in 1914.

Rescuing Species

When a species is close to becoming extinct, it is called an **endangered species**. When a species is close to becoming endangered, it is called a **threatened species**.

The Endangered Species Act was passed in the United States in 1973. It protects plants and animals that are in danger of extinction. Laws also protect their habitats.

Captive breeding programs help rescue endangered species. Wildlife experts capture the endangered species and breed them in captivity. In this way, they can increase the population of an endangered species.

The California condor is in a captive breeding program. Captive breeding can save a species from extinction.

Summary Population size depends on resources, predator-prey relationships, diseases, and competition. List two ways that people work to protect species that are in danger of extinction.

_____

_____

_____

_____

Cause and Effect What are two factors that lead to extinction of a species?

Causes	Effect
1. _____ _____ _____ 2. _____ _____ _____	Species become extinct.

253

Lesson Preview

VOCABULARY

climax community a mature and stable ecosystem *(noun)*

pioneer species one of the first species to colonize new or disturbed land *(noun)*

primary succession the establishment of plant and animal communities in a place where organisms did not live before *(noun)*

secondary succession the process in which a new community replaces an old one after a disturbance *(noun)*

VOCABULARY SKILL: Word Content

Primary means "first," and *secondary* means "second" or "after the first." Read the definitions of *primary succession* and *secondary succession*. What do the words *primary* and *secondary* tell you about the meanings of these terms?

254

2 What Is Ecological Succession?

Ecosystems that have been changed can be brought back to their original condition through ecological succession.

Natural Disturbances

A stable ecosystem can be disturbed or destroyed by earthquakes, volcanic eruptions, floods, and other disasters. The result will be a new ecosystem.

Mount St. Helens, a volcano in the state of Washington, erupted in 1980. An enormous blast of hot gases and ash destroyed millions of trees. Thick ash covered the ground, killing almost all plant life near the volcano.

But life returned to the whole area. Wind blew in seeds of grasses and shrubs. These grew, followed by larger plants. Then animals returned to the area.

A few years after the eruption of Mount St. Helens, flowers bloomed on nearby slopes.

Primary Succession

❶ Volcanic activity creates a new island.

❷ Pioneer species such as mold, bacteria, and visiting sea birds begin to form soil.

❸ Eventually, grasses, shrubs, and other species are able to thrive.

Primary Succession

There are two kinds of succession: primary and secondary. **Primary succession** is the establishment of plant and animal communities on ground where living things have never existed before.

In 1963, an erupting volcano broke through the ocean surface. It formed a new island, called Surtsey, off the coast of Iceland. The island was just a patch of lava. Then primary succession began.

Small, fast-growing plants require few nutrients. They are blown in by the wind. They begin to grow on rock and bare ground. A **pioneer species** is one of the first species to colonize new or disturbed land.

1. List three natural disasters that can destroy a stable ecosystem.

   a. _____

   b. _____

   c. _____

2. Complete the diagram to tell about primary succession.

   Primary Succession

   establishment of plant and animal communities on ground where organisms _____ _____

3. Complete the diagram to show how primary succession takes place.

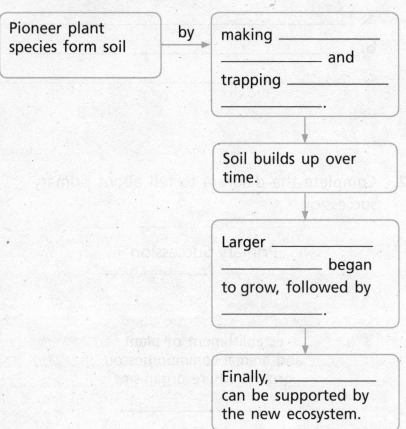

Pioneer plant species form soil

— by →

making _____ _____ and trapping _____ _____ .

↓

Soil builds up over time.

↓

Larger _____ _____ began to grow, followed by _____ .

↓

Finally, _____ can be supported by the new ecosystem.

After a pioneer species starts to thrive in an area, wildflowers and trees can grow.

Pioneer plant species form soil by making acids that break down rock. They also trap soil particles that blow in. Grasses and other small plants can grow as soil builds up over time.

Next, larger plants and shrubs begin to grow. These are followed by trees. Animal life can be supported by this new ecosystem.

On Surtsey, molds and bacteria were pioneer species. They broke down rocks to form soil. The waste of sea birds added nutrients to the soil. Today the island ecosystem has hundreds of species.

Secondary Succession

Fire, landslides, and floods can destroy an ecosystem in hours or even minutes. **Secondary succession** is the regular progression of new communities that form after disturbances such as these.

Secondary succession is quicker than primary succession because soil is already in place. Plants and animals that survived help the process along, too.

Pioneer species are fast-growing grasses and wildflowers. Taller plants follow and then tall trees grow. Over time, a forest of hardwood trees may grow.

Secondary Succession

❶ A forest fire destroys plant life but leaves the soil behind.

❷ Grasses and small plants sprout, followed by young trees.

❸ Young trees grow into tall, mature trees.

4. Complete the diagram to tell about secondary succession.

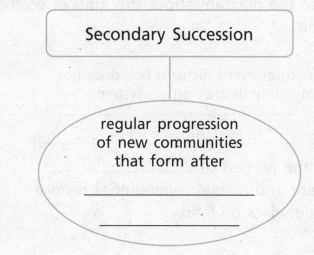

Secondary Succession

regular progression of new communities that form after

_____

_____

I Wonder . . . Why does secondary succession take place at a faster rate than primary succession?

_____

_____

_____

_____

Summary   Ecosystems disturbed by natural events can be restored through ecological succession. Complete the diagram about this kind of ecological succession.

A natural event disturbs but does not completely destroy an ecosystem.

In the process of _____, plant and animal communities restore themselves on land.

Eventually, the ecosystem becomes stable and mature, forming a _____.

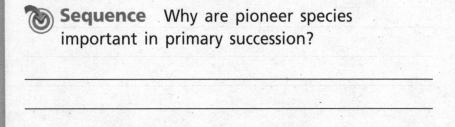

Sequence   Why are pioneer species important in primary succession?

_____

_____

_____

The trees and bushes in this forest will help the process of secondary succession.

The changes of succession take place quickly at first. Over time, the community of plants and animals does not change much; it is stable. A mature ecosystem that remains mostly stable over time is called a **climax community**. Change is slow in a climax community until a new disturbance occurs.

A fire burned most of the trees in some areas of Yellowstone National Park in 1988. Secondary succession was at work after just a few weeks. New seedlings of pine trees began to grow.

SEQUENCE

Why are pioneer species important in primary succession?

How Do Humans Change Ecosystems?

3

Human activities can affect the number and types of living things in an ecosystem.

Human Activities

Rain forests are a valuable resource on Earth. They are home to a wide variety of plants and animals. But much of the rain forest is lost each year.

This is important because plants and animals may become extinct when their habitat is destroyed. Some rain forest plants may be used as medicines. Plants in the rain forest also release oxygen and take in carbon dioxide from the atmosphere.

Humans have the power to save or destroy ecosystems. The rain forest is not the only ecosystem affected by human activity.

Tropical rain forests are cleared for farming and logging. This destroys many species.

VOCABULARY

biodiversity the variety of species that live in an ecosystem *(noun)*

pollution the addition of harmful substances to the environment *(noun)*

VOCABULARY SKILL: Compound Words

In this lesson, you will read about wetlands. *Wetland* is a compound word made from the words *wet* and *land*. Think about the meaning of these words. Now write a definition for the compound word *wetland*.

_____

_____

 5.e. Students know that the number and kinds of living things that an ecosystem can support depends on many factors.

259

1. Complete the diagram to tell about clear-cutting.

Cause		Effects
clear-cutting	→	**a.** destroys _____ and _____ and
		b. causes soil _____

2. List three reasons why we need wetlands.

a. _____

b. _____

c. _____

The top of a hill was cut off to build these houses in California.

Clear-cutting is a problem in many temperate forests in the United States. Clear-cutting means removing every tree from an area. This destroys ecosystems and habitats. Clear-cutting also causes soil erosion.

Wetlands are sometimes drained and filled in so the land can be used for buildings. We need wetlands because they help filter chemicals from rivers and streams. The spongy grasses in wetlands help to reduce flooding. Wetlands are also important for many aquatic animal species.

Pollution

Pollution is the addition of harmful substances to the environment. Certain gases and solid particles, called pollutants, are sent into the air when fossil fuels are burned. Fossil fuels include oil, natural gas, and coal. Pollutants can make the air unhealthy to breathe. Some can combine with water vapor and form acid rain.

Oil is also a threat to the environment. Accidental spills can damage habitats and be expensive to clean up.

WATER POLLUTION
Oil spills can harm plants and animals living in or near the water.

AIR POLLUTION Some factories burn fossil fuels that release harmful gases into the air.

3. What is pollution?

_____

_____

4. Complete the diagram to tell how burning fossil fuels causes acid rain.

```
┌─────────────────────────────────────┐
│ Fossil fuels are burned.            │
└─────────────────────────────────────┘
                  │
                  ▼
┌─────────────────────────────────────┐
│ _____ are sent into the air. │
└─────────────────────────────────────┘
                  │
                  ▼
┌─────────────────────────────────────┐
│ Some _____ combine with water │
│ vapor and form _____.         │
└─────────────────────────────────────┘
```

261

5. List three examples of solid waste.

a. _____

b. _____

c. _____

6. How can farming and lawn care cause pollution?

_____

_____

_____

LAND POLLUTION Trash and garbage pollute the land when they are not disposed of properly.

Human activities also pollute the land. People in the United States produce hundreds of millions of tons of solid waste every year. Solid waste includes paper, plastic, and metals. Solid waste must be burned or buried in landfills. It can harm the environment and many species if it is not disposed of properly.

Some farming and lawn-care practices also cause pollution. Rain can wash fertilizers and pesticides into rivers and streams. They can damage the ecosystem.

Growth of Human Population

Today's human population is very large. It is growing larger all the time. More than 6 billion people live on the planet.

Advances in medicine and technology have allowed more people to survive diseases and accidents. People are also leading longer lives.

Today's human population is huge and is rapidly growing larger. In 1960 there were 3 billion people; today, there are over 6 billion people!

Advances in technology and medicine are the main reason for this population explosion. Improved farming methods have greatly increased the food supply. Medical breakthroughs allow more people to survive disease and accidents. The result is more people and more people living longer.

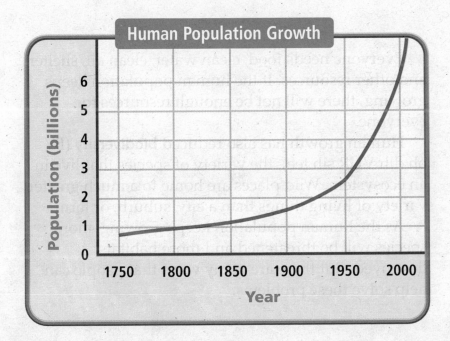

7. Analyze the graph of population data.

   a. (Circle) the point on the graph at which the line crosses the year 1800. What was Earth's population in that year?

   _____

   b. Look again at the line graph. Earth's population doubled between 1800 and 1925, going from 1 billion to 2 billion. How many years did it take for the population to double?

   _____

   c. (Circle) the point on the graph at which Earth's population doubled again; that is, reached 4 billion.
   What year was it? _____

   How many years did it take to double the second time?

   _____

8. Complete the diagram about biodiversity.

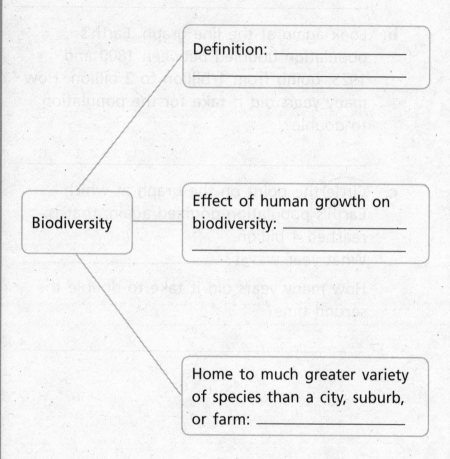

Biodiversity

Definition: _____
_____

Effect of human growth on biodiversity: _____
_____

Home to much greater variety of species than a city, suburb, or farm: _____

A growing human population must compete for a limited amount of resources.

Everyone needs food, clean water, clean air, shelter, and other resources. If the human population keeps growing, there will not be enough resources for everyone.

Human growth has also reduced **biodiversity** (BY oh dih VUR sih tee), the variety of species that live in an ecosystem. Wild places are home to a much greater variety of living things than a city, suburb, or farm.

As the human population keeps growing, more species will be threatened and more habitats destroyed. But there are many ways that people can help solve these problems.

Conservation and Preservation Efforts

People are trying to repair damaged ecosystems and preserve wild places. World governments have set aside many areas as national parks, wildlife refuges, national monuments, and wilderness areas.

There are hundreds of parks that protect ecosystems, wildlife, and special landscapes. The Liberty Prairie Reserve protects tallgrass prairie, wetland, and oak savannah in Illinois. It is home to 21 threatened and endangered species.

Some preserves are in the ocean. They protect marine species. Zoos help, too. They run captive breeding programs to save some species and restore others.

A baby panda born in a zoo receives good care.

Muir Woods is a woodland preserve that protects native redwood trees.

9. List three ways that people preserve ecosystems.

a. _____

b. _____

c. _____

I Wonder . . . The human population keeps growing. What effect will this have on people and other organisms?

_____

_____

_____

_____

265

10. Complete the diagram to tell about biodiversity hotspots.

Biodiversity hotspots

What are they? _____

_____

Why should they be protected?

_____

_____

Percentage of world's mammals that they contain:

_____

11. On the map, circle the two biodiversity hotspots that are mentioned in the text.

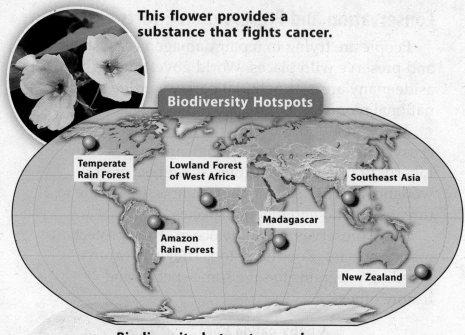

This flower provides a substance that fights cancer.

Biodiversity Hotspots

Temperate Rain Forest

Lowland Forest of West Africa

Southeast Asia

Madagascar

Amazon Rain Forest

New Zealand

Biodiversity hotspots are places where many plant and animal species are threatened with extinction.

Some areas of the world are rich in plant and animal diversity. This means that there are many different plant and animal species. These areas are called biodiversity hotspots. They are threatened by human activities.

The Amazon rain forest is a well-known example of a biodiversity hotspot. Another biodiversity hotspot is Madagascar, an island off the coast of Africa.

Scientists think that biodiversity hotspots contain more than 80 percent of the world's mammals. Biodiversity hotspots must be protected to save plants and animals for the benefit of people in the future.

Saving the Salton Sea

The Salton Sea is a large, salty lake in California's Colorado Desert. The sea and its wetlands are important desert ecosystems. Many fish and birds live there. It is also a stopover point for migrating birds.

The sea is fed mostly by salty runoff from the farm fields around it. Several changes threaten its survival and its ability to support life.

The Salton Sea has been shrinking and getting saltier. The lives of fish and birds are threatened. Government officials have suggested solutions, such as canals to bring in freshwater. The concentration of salt in the water must be lowered to save the Salton Sea.

The health of the black-necked stilt depends on the health of the Salton Sea.

Reduced runoff from nearby fields has shrunk the Salton Sea and made it saltier.

MAIN IDEA

What have governments done to help protect ecosystems?

Summary Human activities can affect the number and types of organisms an ecosystem can support. How are people trying to save the Salton Sea?

_____

_____

_____

Main Idea What have governments done to help protect ecosystems?

To help protect ecosystems, governments have set aside special areas.

267

Group two or more words on the page and explain why they go together.

_____

_____

_____

_____

_____

biodiversity (BY oh dih VUR sih tee) the variety of species that live in an ecosystem

> **biodiversidad** variedad de especies que vive en un ecosistema

climax community a mature and stable ecosystem

> **comunidad estable** ecosistema maduro que se mantiene estable

competition the struggle among living things to use the same resources in an ecosystem

> **competencia** lucha entre seres vivos por usar los mismos recursos de un ecosistema

disease a condition that prevents an organism from functioning properly

> **enfermedad** afección que impide que un organismo funcione correctamente

endangered species a species that is close to becoming extinct

> **especie en peligro** especie que está cerca de extinguirse

extinction the complete disappearance of a species

> **extinción** desaparición total de una especie

invasive species plants or animals that are not native to an ecosystem

> **especie invasiva** planta o animal que no son nativos de un ecosistema

limiting factor something that restricts the growth and distribution of a population

> **factor limitante** algo que restringe el crecimiento y la distribución de una población

Glossary

pioneer species one of the first species to colonize new or disturbed land

especie pionera una de las primeras especies en colonizar tierras nuevas o conocidas

pollution the addition of harmful substances to the environment

contaminación liberación de sustancias perjudiciales en el medio ambiente

predation when one organism—the predator—catches and feeds on another organism—the prey

conducta predatoria cuando un organismo, el depredador, caza y se alimenta de otro organismo, la presa

primary succession the establishment of plant and animal communities in a place where organisms did not live before

sucesión primaria establecimiento de comunidades animales o vegetales en lugares donde anteriormente no vivían organismos

secondary succession the process in which a new community replaces an old one after a disturbance

sucesión secundaria proceso mediante el cual una comunidad nueva remplaza a otra antigua después de una alteración

threatened species a species that is close to becoming endangered

especie amenazada especie que está cercana a la extinción

 Visit www.eduplace.com to play puzzles and word games.

⬭Circle the English words and their meanings for all glossary terms containing the word *species*.

269

Chapter Review

WHAT DID YOU LEARN?

Vocabulary

❶ (Circle) the correct answer on the page.

Comprehension

❷ _____
_____

❸ _____
_____
_____

❹ _____
_____

Critical Thinking

❺ _____
_____
_____
_____
_____

Responding

Think About What You Have Read

Vocabulary

❶ The variety of species in an ecosystem is called
_____.

    A) competition

    B) a climax community

    C) biodiversity

    D) commensalism

Comprehension

❷ What happens to prey populations when predator populations rise?

❸ Explain the difference between primary and secondary succession.

❹ How are people harming ecosystems?

Critical Thinking

❺ How would you improve chances of keeping invasive species out of North America? Is this an important goal? Explain your answer.

KWL

WHAT DO YOU KNOW?

List three energy sources that you use every day.

a. _____

b. _____

c. _____

Energy Resources

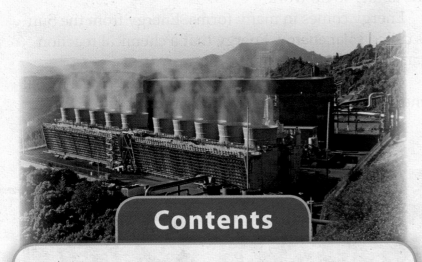

Contents

WHAT DO YOU WANT TO KNOW?
What questions do you have about how people use energy?

_____

_____

Write a question that you have about fossil fuels or their alternatives.

_____

_____

What other questions do you have about energy resources?

_____

_____

VOCABULARY

efficiency the amount of work a machine does compared to the amount of energy put into the machine *(noun)*

energy the ability to do work *(noun)*

solar energy energy from the Sun *(noun)*

VOCABULARY SKILL: Prefixes

In this lesson, you will learn about energy transformations. The word *transformation* has the prefix *trans-*, which means "so as to change." The base word *formation* means "the act of giving shape." Use these meanings to write your own definition of *transformation*.

_____

_____

1 How Do People Use Energy?

Energy takes many forms. Energy can be changed from one form to another, but energy cannot be made or destroyed.

Energy Transformations

What is energy? Energy is a basic part of the universe. It is everywhere. Scientists define **energy** as the ability to do work.

Energy comes in many forms. Energy from the Sun is called **solar energy**. Energy that a chemical reaction can release is called chemical energy.

Energy from position or motion is called mechanical energy. A coiled spring has mechanical energy.

Energy Changes at a Cookout

Chemical energy is changed into thermal energy when wood burns.

Energy Changes in a Car

This car burns gas in its engine. Chemical energy in gas is changed into mechanical energy.

3.a. Students know that energy can be carried from one place to another.
3.b. Students know that using fuel releases mostly heat energy.

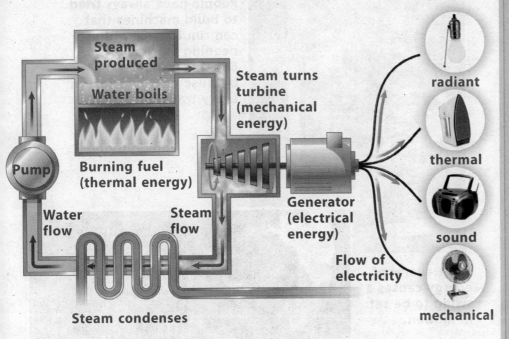

radiant

thermal

sound

mechanical

Steam produced

Water boils

Steam turns turbine (mechanical energy)

Pump

Burning fuel (thermal energy)

Water flow

Steam flow

Generator (electrical energy)

Flow of electricity

Steam condenses

Thermal energy from fuel is changed into electrical energy at a power plant.

Energy can be changed, or transformed, from one form to another. Thermal energy is released when energy is transformed.

Electricity is another form of energy. Electrical energy is changed into other forms in light bulbs, toasters, and radios. Modern technology runs on energy that changes form.

Energy transformations also take place in nature. The Sun warms Earth and powers weather. Plants use solar energy from the Sun to grow.

1. What type of energy is released when energy is transformed?

   _____

2. List three types of technology that transform electrical energy into other forms of energy.

   a. _____

   b. _____

   c. _____

3. List three ways that energy is transformed in nature.

   a. The Sun _____ Earth.

   b. The Sun _____ weather.

   c. Plants use _____ energy from the Sun to grow.

4. Complete the diagram to explain how mechanical energy is changed into thermal energy.

> You push your friend on a swing. The force of your push gives the swing and its rider _____ _____.

⬇

> Mechanical energy is changed into _____ _____ at the points where the swing rubs against its hooks.

5. List the two ideas that make up the law of conservation of energy.

a. _____

_____

b. _____

_____

People have always tried to build machines that can run forever without needing more energy. But this is impossible because energy is lost in every transformation.

The transfer of energy causes a swing to be set in motion.

Conservation of Energy

In every energy transformation, some energy is lost as thermal energy. Think about pushing a friend on a swing. The force of your push gives the swing and its rider mechanical energy. If you could feel the hooks where the chain is attached, they would feel hot. Some mechanical energy of the moving swing is changed into thermal energy.

A closed system is a system in which energy cannot enter or exit. Energy can change form, but energy cannot be made or destroyed. These two ideas make up the law of conservation of energy.

Energy Efficiency

Some thermal energy is always released when energy changes form. As a result, most machines are not very energy efficient.

The **efficiency** of a machine compares the amount of work a machine does to the amount of energy put into the machine. No machine can be 100-percent efficient.

Energy efficiency can be improved. Power plants can reduce friction in turbines and generators. They can also reduce energy losses along power lines. Customers can use energy-saving items, such as fluorescent lights.

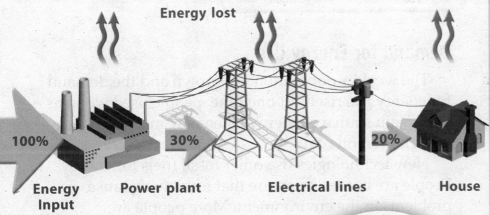

Energy lost

100%   30%   20%

Energy   Power plant   Electrical lines   House
Input

Energy is converted from one form to another. Some energy is lost as thermal energy at each step.

6. Complete the diagram about energy efficiency.

> Efficiency compares

> the amount of _____ a machine does

> with the amount of _____ put into the machine.

I Wonder . . . When is thermal energy a desirable product?

_____

_____

_____

_____

_____

_____

_____

_____

Summary   Fossil fuels and other energy sources power modern technology. How has the use of fossil fuels (petroleum, natural gas, and coal) changed over the past 200 years?

_____

_____

_____

_____

Draw Conclusions   How might conditions on Earth be different if solar energy could not change form?

_____

_____

_____

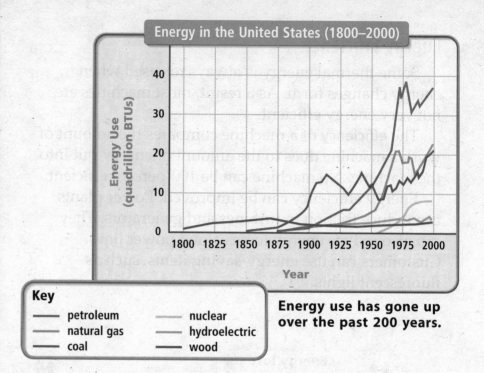

Energy in the United States (1800–2000)

Energy Use (quadrillion BTUs)

40

30

20

10

0

1800 1825 1850 1875 1900 1925 1950 1975 2000

Year

Key

— petroleum
— natural gas
— coal
— nuclear
— hydroelectric
— wood

Energy use has gone up over the past 200 years.

Demand for Energy Use

The world's population has grown and the demand for energy has risen. At one time, people used wood as their main source of energy. Then new machines and factories ran on coal.

New technologies use other fossil fuels for energy. People are becoming aware that fossil fuels cause problems in the environment. More people are becoming interested in better energy sources, such as hydroelectric energy and nuclear energy.

DRAW CONCLUSIONS

How might conditions on Earth be different if solar energy could not change form?

Why Are Fossil Fuels Limited?

Fossil fuels formed over millions of years from the remains of plants and animals. People depend on fossil fuels for energy. Fossil fuels can harm the environment.

Formation of Fossil Fuels

During the 1700s, machines were powered by coal. Later, people found that oil and gas were useful energy sources. All these resources came from fossil fuels.

Fossil fuels are energy resources formed from the remains of plants and animals that lived more than 100 million years ago. The main fossil fuels are coal, petroleum or oil, and natural gas.

The plants of ancient swamps died and became fossil fuels.

VOCABULARY

conservation the efficient use of resources *(noun)*

fossil fuels energy resources formed from the remains of plants and animals that lived more than 100 million years ago *(noun)*

natural resource a material found in nature that people use, such as soil, air, water, and fossil fuels *(noun)*

nonrenewable resource a resource that cannot be replaced quickly or easily, such as fossil fuels *(noun)*

VOCABULARY SKILL: Prefixes/Suffixes

The word *conservation* has the suffix *-tion*, which means "action." The base word *conserve* means "to preserve or protect." Read the definition of *conservation* above. Then use the word *conservation* in a sentence.

_____

_____

_____

 3.b. Students know that using fuel releases mostly heat energy.
6.a. Students know that some energy sources are more useful than others.

1. Fill in the diagram with the steps for the formation of coal.

Dead organic matter builds up in swamps and forms peat.

↓

Peat is _____ under layers of soil and _____. The water is pressed out. The type of coal formed by this process is called _____.

↓

_____ causes the material to change into _____ coal.

↓

High _____ and _____ can cause the material to change into _____ coal.

Long ago, Earth's climate was warm and the land was covered with swamps and shallow seas. Huge ferns and trees grew in the swamps. These plants died off and were buried under mud and other sediments. Animals also died and were buried in the swamps.

Over time, pressure compacted the remains. Pressure and high temperature caused the remains to eventually change to coal.

Today, deposits of fossil fuels are mined all over the world, including California.

Coal Formation

Peat

1. Dead organic matter builds up in thick swamps. It is called peat.

Lignite

2. Peat is buried under layers of soil and sediment. The water is pressed out of the peat.

Bituminous coal

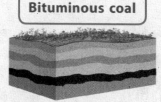

3. Pressure causes the material to change into bituminous coal.

Anthracite

4. High pressure and temperature can cause the material to change into anthracite coal.

Burning Fossil Fuels

You have read that plants use energy from the Sun to make food. Fossil fuels are also a part of an energy chain that begins with the Sun.

Energy from the Sun is stored in fossil fuels. The energy is released when fossil fuels are burned.

Some fossil fuels are used to run factories. Generators change mechanical energy into electrical energy. Others are burned in engines. Engines change chemical energy into mechanical energy.

Miners use heavy machinery to dig out underground coal deposits.

Coal

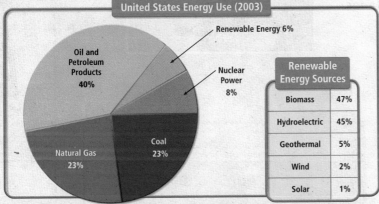

United States Energy Use (2003)

Renewable Energy 6%

Oil and Petroleum Products 40%

Nuclear Power 8%

Natural Gas 23%

Coal 23%

Renewable Energy Sources	
Biomass	47%
Hydroelectric	45%
Geothermal	5%
Wind	2%
Solar	1%

This pie chart shows that most of the energy used in the United States comes from nonrenewable resources.

2. Energy from the _____ is stored in _____ fuels.

3. Complete the table to summarize fossil fuel use.

Factories	Engines
Generators change _____ energy into _____ energy.	Engines change _____ energy into _____ energy.

4. Look at the pie chart. Circle the fossil fuels. How much energy use in the United States depends on these fossil fuels?

_____

5. Explain why fossil fuels may not be the best choice for meeting energy needs.

_____

_____

_____

6. List two uses of fossil fuels.

a. _____

_____

b. _____

_____

Fossil fuels are also used for heat. Natural gas is used to heat half of all the homes in the United States.

Fossil fuels may not be the best choice for meeting all these energy needs. One problem is that fossil fuels are a **nonrenewable resource**, meaning they cannot be replaced quickly or easily.

People use fossil fuels much more quickly than nature can replace them. Earth's supply of fossil fuels will run out if the rate of use stays the same.

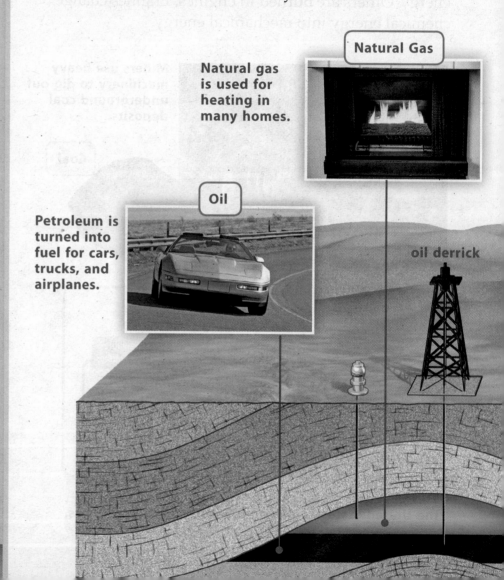

Natural Gas

Natural gas is used for heating in many homes.

Oil

Petroleum is turned into fuel for cars, trucks, and airplanes.

oil derrick

Burning fossil fuels also pollutes the environment. Today, strict laws and better technology help reduce pollution from fossil fuels. But air pollution from factories and cars is still a serious problem. Burning fossil fuels releases carbon dioxide gases into the air.

The carbon dioxide gases may change Earth's atmosphere. Many scientists argue that it is causing global temperatures to rise slowly. This is called global warming.

Coal

Coal is used as an energy source in factories and power plants.

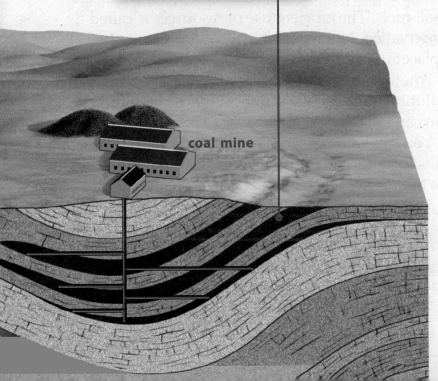

coal mine

7. Explain how burning fossil fuels harms the environment.

_____

_____

_____

_____

_____

Summary Fossil fuels are a nonrenewable natural resource. List three ways to conserve Earth's resources.

a. _____

b. _____

c. _____

 Problem and Solution What problems can conservation help solve?

Problems	Solution
a. _____ b. _____	conserving resources

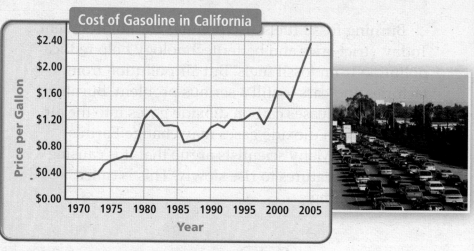

Cost of Gasoline in California

Price per Gallon: $2.40, $2.00, $1.60, $1.20, $0.80, $0.40, $0.00

Year: 1970 1975 1980 1985 1990 1995 2000 2005

Most cars run on gas. Gas is made from petroleum. The cost of gas is expected to rise as petroleum reserves are used up.

Conservation of Fossil Fuels

Natural resources are products and materials found in nature that people use, such as soil, air, water, and fossil fuels. The efficient use of resources is called **conservation**. Nonrenewable resources cannot be replaced. This is why conserving them is so important.

Another reason to conserve fossil fuels is to reduce pollution. Polluted air is unhealthy to breathe. Acid rain can kill trees and fish.

You can help conserve Earth's resources. Use public transportation, or form carpools. Turn off lights when not in use. Recycle materials such as paper, plastic, and metals.

PROBLEM AND SOLUTION

What problems can conservation help to solve?

What Are Alternatives to Fossil Fuels?

3

People are finding ways to use renewable energy resources to replace fossil fuels. Some renewable sources are solar energy, wind, biomass, and geothermal energy.

The Importance of Renewable Energy

Renewable sources of energy may solve energy needs for the future. **Renewable resources**, such as the Sun, wind, and moving water, can be used day after day without running out. Renewable resources do not pollute the atmosphere.

There are a few problems with renewable resources. Some are limited to certain areas. Others need expensive technology. But many renewable resources hold the promise for energy in the future.

Solar PV cells were used to run this Mars Rover as it explored Mars.

VOCABULARY

biomass once-living matter *(noun)*

geothermal energy thermal energy from Earth's interior *(noun)*

hydroelectric energy electric energy generated from moving water *(noun)*

nuclear fission a process in which nuclei of uranium or similar elements are split apart, releasing vast amounts of energy *(noun)*

renewable resource a resource, such as the Sun, wind, and moving water, that can be used day after day without running out *(noun)*

solar energy energy from the Sun *(noun)*

VOCABULARY SKILL: Word Origins

The word *geothermal* comes from two Greek words: *geō-* which means "earth" or "soil," and *thermē-*, which means "heat." In your own words, explain what *geothermal* means.

_____

_____

 3.a. Students know that using fuel releases mostly heat energy.
6.a. Students know that energy can be carried from one place to another.

285

1. What is a renewable resource?

_____

_____

2. Follow the arrows on the diagram. Then complete the sentences to explain how solar energy can be "caught" and used.

| _____ _____ heats water inside the _____ _____. |

↓

| The _____ water then goes to the _____ _____. |

↓

| Cold water comes into the house and is pumped into the _____ _____. The hot water from the _____ _____ heats the cold water. |

↓

| The heated water is then used in different ways inside the house. |

Solar Energy

The Sun supplies **solar energy**, an inexhaustible energy source. This means people can never use it up. It does not cause pollution. But using solar energy can be expensive.

The diagram below shows one way to "catch" and use solar energy. Solar energy can be used to heat water for a house. Solar energy can also be used to make electricity in solar power plants.

Photovoltaic cells, or PV cells, collect light and change it directly into electricity. Today, PV cells are used to power calculators, home appliances, and even spacecraft.

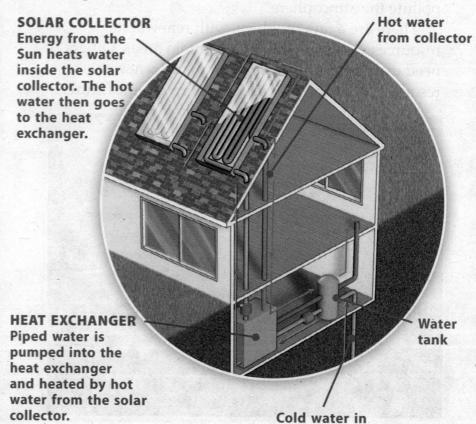

SOLAR COLLECTOR
Energy from the Sun heats water inside the solar collector. The hot water then goes to the heat exchanger.

Hot water from collector

Water tank

HEAT EXCHANGER
Piped water is pumped into the heat exchanger and heated by hot water from the solar collector.

Cold water in

Wind Power

Wind power is a promising source of electricity. Wind spins the blades of a turbine. Mechanical energy is turned into electrical energy.

Wind energy does have some drawbacks. Wind turbines work best in places where winds blow steadily. Wind farms, areas with dozens of turbines, take up a lot of space. They are also noisy. Many wind farms are in desert lands or other areas without many people.

Winds blow because the Sun heats Earth unevenly. This means the source of wind power is solar energy.

Shaft

Gear box

Generator

Blade

A wind turbine can be as tall as a 20-story building.

3. Describe how the energy of wind is "caught."

Cause		Effect
Winds spins the blades of a _____.	→	_____ energy is turned into _____ energy.

4. What is the source of wind power?

_____

I Wonder . . . What are some of the potential disadvantages of wind power?

_____

_____

_____

_____

_____

_____

287

5. Explain how hydroelectric energy is made.

> A hydroelectric power plant begins with a
> _____. _____ is stored behind
> this feature.

↓

> Water runs through _____ and spins
> _____.

↓

> _____ from the spinning turbines is
> converted to _____.

Energy from Moving Water

Electric energy generated from moving water is called **hydroelectric energy**. A hydroelectric power plant begins with a dam. Water is stored behind the dam. Then water runs through tunnels and spins turbines. The energy from the spinning turbines is converted into electricity.

Hydroelectric plants make energy without polluting the air. They also depend on the water cycle. The water cycle is a free energy resource.

The Annapolis Tidal Generating Station uses turbines to generate electricity.

The Itaipu Dam is on the Parana River. It is one of the largest hydroelectric power plants in the world.

There are some problems with this type of power plant. Hydroelectric plants can damage river ecosystems. Large dams can change the flow of the river and harm fish and other animals. A series of dams can disrupt fish migration.

The moving water in ocean tides can also be used for energy. Water is trapped behind a dam during high tide. When the tide goes out, the water passes over turbines. Tidal power plants work best in places where there is a big difference between high tide and low tide.

6. Compare and contrast the advantages and disadvantages of hydroelectric energy.

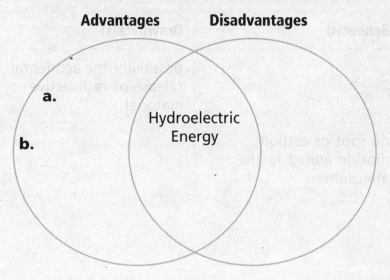

7. Complete the steps for making energy through the use of ocean tides.

a. Water is trapped behind a dam during _____ tide.

b. When the tide goes _____, the water passes over _____.

c. These plants work best in areas where there is a _____ difference between high tide and _____ tide.

289

8. Explain the benefits and drawbacks of nuclear fission.

Benefit(s)	Drawback(s)
	possibility for accidental release of radioactive material
no soot or carbon dioxide added to the atmosphere	

9. (Circle) *steam* in the diagram. Tell how steam helps make nuclear energy.

_____

_____

_____

Nuclear Energy

In a nuclear power plant, nuclei of uranium or plutonium are split in a controlled process called **nuclear fission**. This process makes a lot of energy.

The energy made from fission is used to boil water. This makes steam. The steam turns turbines that turn generators to make electricity.

Nuclear power plants offer a clean, quiet way to make electricity. They do not add soot or carbon dioxide to the atmosphere. However, the accidental release of radioactive material is a big risk of this type of energy. Nuclear waste is another common problem.

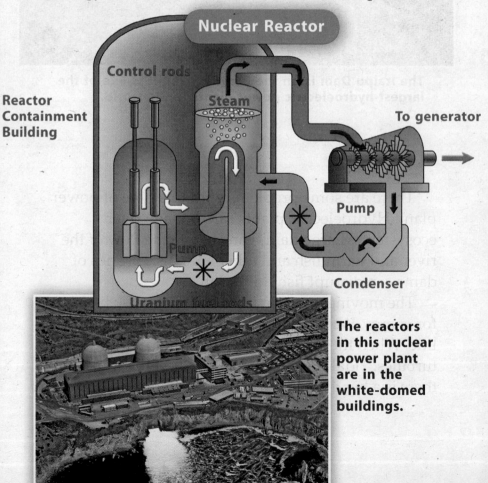

Nuclear Reactor

Control rods

Steam

To generator

Reactor Containment Building

Pump

Pump

Condenser

Uranium fuel rods

The reactors in this nuclear power plant are in the white-domed buildings.

Geothermal Energy

Thermal energy from Earth's interior is called **geothermal energy**. Some magma inside Earth is near underground pools of water. Extremely hot water and steam rise through rocks to the surface.

The heated water can be used to produce electricity. In geothermal power plants, steam or hot water is carried through underground pipes. The steam turns turbines that turn generators. The water can be sent back down to be heated again.

Geothermal energy is a free source of energy that will not run out. Geothermal power plants work best at Earth's "hot spots."

Turbine Generator

Steam Electricity

Geothermal power plants change mechanical energy into electrical energy.

10. How is water heated inside Earth?

_____

_____

_____

_____

11. How is geothermal energy used in a power plant?

_____

_____

12. Make the following statement *true*.

Geothermal energy costs money and will one day run out.

_____

_____

291

13. Once-living matter is called biomass. Where does biomass come from?

a. _____

b. _____

c. _____

d. _____

e. _____

14. How is biomass used to produce energy?

_____

_____

Biomass

Each year, many tons of once-living matter, or **biomass**, go to waste. Biomass is unused plant parts from farms, sawdust and bark from lumber mills, food scraps, and animal wastes. Wood is another form of biomass.

Biomass comes from living matter, so it contains stored energy. New technologies are needed to make biomass a cost-efficient energy source.

Biomass can be burned in a power plant to make electricity. Another way to use biomass is to let it decay on farms or in landfills. Biomass produces a fuel called methane gas as it decays.

Ethanol

Corn can be made into a fuel called ethanol. Many gas stations sell gas mixed with ethanol.

SUPER UNLEADED

PRICE PER GALLON $

89

CONTAINS ETHANOL BLEND 10%

Composting is a great way to conserve resources in your backyard.

Biomass can be used to make another kind of fuel. Unwanted parts of corn plants can be used to make ethanol, a type of alcohol. Ethanol can also be burned as fuel.

Biomass causes much less air pollution than fossil fuels when it is burned. Using biomass for energy also saves space in landfills.

Another use for biomass is composting. You can place grass clippings, fruit rinds, and potato peels into a compost bin or pile. When these materials decay, they turn into a nutrient-rich fertilizer.

15. (Circle) the biomass in the photos on these pages. Then tell how biomass can be used for fuel and fertilizer.

Fuel: _____

_____

Fertilizer: _____

_____

16. List two ways in which biomass helps protect the environment.

a. _____

_____

b. _____

_____

17. List two alternative fuels used to power vehicles.

a. _____

b. _____

18. Describe alternative power sources and their uses.

Alternative Power Source	How It Is Used
	runs subways and many buses
gasoline and battery-powered engine	
	make energy from hydrogen and oxygen

Alternative Fuels for Vehicles

One key to conserving petroleum is developing and using alternative fuels. Scientists are working on engines that run on ethanol only. Some car engines can use vegetable oil as fuel!

Today, subways and many buses run on electricity. Hybrid electric cars use both a small gasoline engine and a motor that runs on batteries. Hydrogen fuel cells are another alternative power source. They use hydrogen and oxygen to make a lot of energy.

Alternative Fuels

Hydrogen fuel cells are used on spacecraft to power electric equipment.

Diesel engines can be converted to run on used vegetable oil.

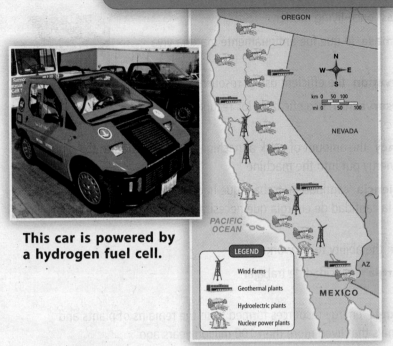

Sources of Alternative Energy in California

This car is powered by a hydrogen fuel cell.

LEGEND

Wind farms
Geothermal plants
Hydroelectric plants
Nuclear power plants

OREGON

NEVADA

PACIFIC OCEAN

AZ

MEXICO

N
W · E
S

km 0   50   100
mi 0   50   100

Renewable Energy in California

California depends on fossil fuels for its energy needs. But alternative energy sources are growing. California uses hydroelectric energy, nuclear power, and renewable energy sources, such as solar, wind, and geothermal energy.

California also supports the use of "plug-in" hybrid cars. These vehicles use larger batteries and can travel longer distances on electric power instead of gas. The goal is a hybrid vehicle that is pollution-free.

MAIN IDEA

How can moving water be a source of electricity?

Summary   Fossil fuels are nonrenewable, and the supply of them is limited. They also pollute the environment. For these reasons, people are developing ways to use renewable energy resources. Complete the diagram to summarize uses of alternative energy in California.

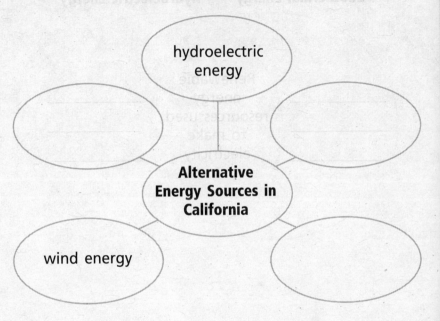

hydroelectric energy

Alternative Energy Sources in California

wind energy

Main Idea   How can moving water be a source of electricity?

_____

_____

Read the definitions of *geothermal energy* and *hydroelectric energy*. Complete the diagram to compare and contrast these two words.

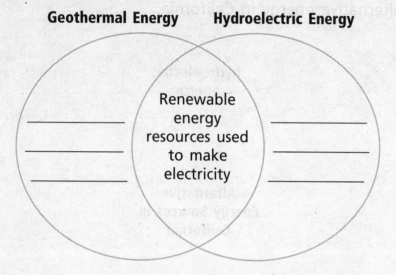

Geothermal Energy   Hydroelectric Energy

Renewable energy resources used to make electricity

_____

_____

_____

_____

_____

_____

296

biomass once-living matter

> **biomasa** lo que fue antiguamente materia viva

conservation the efficient use of resources

> **conservación** uso eficaz de los recursos

efficiency the amount of work a machine does compared to the amount of energy put into the machine

> **eficiencia** cantidad de trabajo que hace una máquina en comparación con la cantidad de energía que necesita

energy the ability to do work

> **energía** capacidad de trabajar

fossil fuels energy resources formed from the remains of plants and animals that lived more than 100 million years ago

> **combustibles fósiles** recursos energéticos que se forman con los restos de animales que vivieron hace más de 100 millones de años

geothermal energy thermal energy from Earth's interior

> **energía geotérmica** energía térmica del interior de la Tierra

hydroelectric energy electric energy generated from moving water

> **energía hidroeléctrica** energía eléctrica generada por el agua en movimiento

Glossary

natural resource a material found in nature that people use, such as soil, air, water, and fossil fuels

recurso natural material que se encuentra en la naturaleza y que la gente usa, como el suelo, el aire, el agua y los combustibles fósiles

nonrenewable resource a resource that cannot be replaced quickly or easily, such as fossil fuels

recurso no renovable recurso que no se puede remplazar rápida o fácilmente, como los combustibles fósiles

nuclear fission a process in which nuclei of uranium or similar elements are split apart, releasing vast amounts of energy

fisión nuclear proceso en el cual los núcleos del uranio y otros elementos similares se separan y liberan grandes cantidades de energía

renewable resource a resource, such as the Sun, wind, and moving water, that can be used day after day without running out.

recurso renovable un recurso como el sol, el viento y el agua en movimiento que se puede usar día tras día sin que se agote

solar energy energy from the Sun

enegía solar energía del Sol

 Visit www.eduplace.com to play puzzles and word games.

Ⓒircle the English words and their meanings for all the glossary words.

Chapter Review

WHAT DID YOU LEARN?

Vocabulary

❶ (Circle) the correct answer on the page.

Comprehension

❷ _____

_____

_____

❸ _____

_____

❹ _____

_____

_____

Critical Thinking

❺ _____

_____

_____

Think About What You Have Read

Vocabulary

❶ Cars that run on ethanol are using the energy stored in _____.

   A) natural gas

   B) biomass

   C) fuel cells

   D) nuclear fuels

Comprehension

❷ Describe the law of conservation of energy.

❸ What are two ways to reduce the pollution that fossil fuels cause?

❹ How can renewable energy resources be used to make electricity?

Critical Thinking

❺ How did the information in this chapter change the way you think about energy in your daily life?

298

K W L

WHAT DO YOU KNOW?

List one fact about each of the following topics.

a. Nonrenewable Resources

_____

_____

b. Renewable Resources

_____

_____

Material Resources

Contents

KWL

WHAT DO YOU WANT TO KNOW?

Skim the photos and headings in this chapter. List one thing that you want to find out about each of these topics.

a. Nonrenewable Resources

_____

_____

b. Renewable Resources

_____

_____

_____

What else do you want to know about Earth's resources?

_____

_____

_____

Lesson Preview

VOCABULARY

material resource things from Earth that can be used to make new products *(noun)*

mineral a solid crystalline chemical element or compound that occurs naturally in Earth's crust *(noun)*

ore a rock that contains enough of a useful mineral to make it valuable *(noun)*

recycling recovering a resource from one item and using that resource to make another item *(noun)*

VOCABULARY SKILL: Prefixes

The prefix *re-* can mean "again" when added to a word. How does knowing this prefix help you understand the meaning of *recycling*?

_____

_____

_____

_____

6.b. Students know that energy and material resources can be classified as renewable or nonrenewable.
6.c. Students know where materials used to make common objects come from in nature.

302

1 What Material Resources Are Nonrenewable?

Many of Earth's resources cannot be replaced. Once they are gone, they are gone forever.

Minerals and Ores

Earth provides a huge variety of **material resources**, which are things from Earth that can be used to make new products. Material resources are either renewable or nonrenewable. Renewable resources can be replaced. Nonrenewable resources cannot be replaced.

One kind of nonrenewable resource is a mineral. A **mineral** is a solid crystalline chemical element or compound that occurs naturally in Earth's crust. Metals such as iron, copper, and gold are kinds of minerals. Minerals are nonrenewable. They take thousands of years to form deep beneath Earth's surface.

Miners dig deep into Earth or strip layers off the surface to uncover minerals.

Uses of Minerals and Ores

Minerals		Ores	
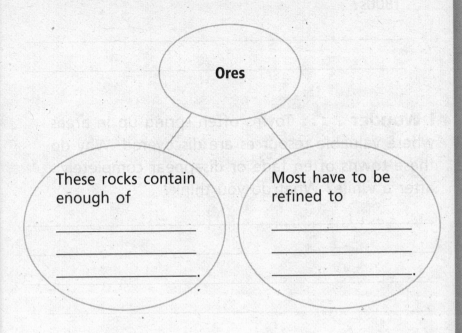	**Fluorite** Uses: Steel, glass, fiberglass, pottery, enamel		**Nickel ore** Uses: Stainless steel, aircraft, electrical equipment
	Gypsum Uses: Wallboard, plaster		**Iron ore** Uses: Steel for cars, railroad tracks, tools, buildings
	Quartz Uses: Glass, radios, clocks, computer chips		**Copper Ore** Uses: Electrical wiring, roofing materials, coins, pipes

Minerals combine to form rocks. An **ore** is a rock that contains enough of some mineral to make it useful.

Most ores must be refined to separate the desired minerals from unwanted materials. Refining ores is a difficult and expensive process.

Minerals have been used to make tools, weapons, dyes, and jewelry. Today, many different minerals are used in different ways. You can see how minerals are used on the chart above.

1. Complete the diagram about ores.

Ores

These rocks contain enough of

_____

_____

_____

Most have to be refined to

_____

_____

_____

2. Circle the word *quartz* on the chart. List four uses of quartz.

a. _____

b. _____

c. _____

d. _____

3. Why did many people come to California in the 1800s?

_____

_____

I Wonder . . . Towns often spring up in areas where valuable resources are discovered. Why do these towns often fade or disappear completely after a while? What do you think?

_____

_____

_____

_____

Where the Resources Are

In the past, people often lived in areas near important natural resources. Settlers moved to California in the mid-1800s when gold was discovered in the state. Towns grew almost overnight. Many of these mining towns struggled when the gold ran out.

In the 1850s, oil was discovered in Pennsylvania. Towns and oil wells sprang up all over the area. Pennsylvania produced half of the world's oil until the Texas oil boom of 1901.

The hunt for gold in the 1800s brought many people to California.

Crude oil is shipped to refineries and made into gasoline and other products.

Today, people depend on resources from all over the world. Resources are shipped over long distances.

The world uses coal, oil, and other fossil fuels for most of its energy needs. Large deposits of these fuels are found in only a few places. Oil is transported by large ships called tankers. Tankers bring the oil to refineries. The finished products are driven by truck to gas stations and other places where they are needed.

4. List the resources that the world uses to meet much of its energy needs.

 a. _____

 b. _____

 c. _____

5. Describe how oil gets from oil fields to the places where it is needed.

 _____

 _____

 _____

305

6. List two problems related to the shipment of oil and other resources.

a. _____

b. _____

7. Find the general location of California on the map. (Circle) one of the resources found there. Use the key to identify the resource you circled. What is one resource found in California?

_____

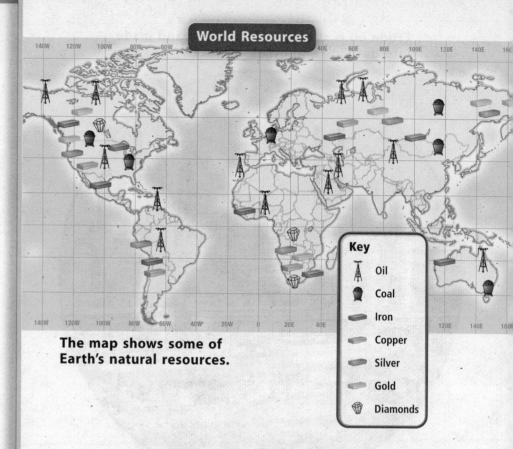

World Resources

The map shows some of Earth's natural resources.

Key

- ⚒ Oil
- ⬤ Coal
- ▬ Iron
- ▬ Copper
- ▬ Silver
- ▬ Gold
- ◈ Diamonds

One problem with shipping oil is that tankers sometimes spill their cargo. It is also expensive to ship resources. It costs a lot of money and energy to ship products any distance.

But the world's system of transportation has made modern life possible. You may wear clothes made from cotton that was grown in Brazil. The aluminum in a can of tuna fish may have come from Australia. Look at the map above to see where other resources come from.

Recycling and Conservation

Recycling means recovering a resource from one item and using that resource to make another item. Recycling conserves resources and saves energy. To conserve resources means to use them wisely.

Lots of everyday items can be recycled: plastic, water bottles, cereal boxes, newspapers, and magazines. You can recycle nonrenewable resources, such as plastic and aluminum, and renewable resources, such as paper products.

Recycling

The triple-arrow symbol means that this can should be recycled.

8. List two recyclable items in each category.

Items to Recycle

Paper
a. _____
_____
b. _____
_____

Plastic
a. _____
_____
b. _____
_____

Metal
a. _____
_____
b. _____
_____

I Wonder . . . How can you tell that an item is recyclable?

_____

_____

9. Complete the chart to provide examples of recycled items.

Used Item	Recycled Item
	new plastic container
aluminum can	
paper product	

10. Analyze the graph. List the recycling rates of the products listed below. Then (circle) the item with the highest rate.

Beverage Cans _____

Plastic Bottles _____

Newspapers _____

Glass Containers _____

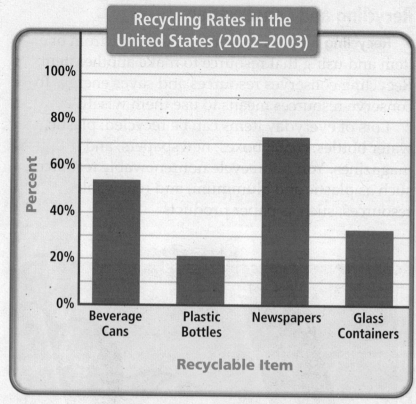

This chart shows the percentages of items that are often recycled.

How are items recycled? The plastic from a water bottle can be melted and molded to form another plastic container. Aluminum cans are melted down to make new aluminum cans. Paper products can be processed to make new paper. Even motor oil from a car can be recycled!

Look for the recycling label on the things that you buy. You are helping to conserve useful resources when you recycle.

The Three R's of Conservation

Three important ways to conserve resources all begin with the letter R. They are reduce, reuse, and recycle.

Reducing simply means using less material. You reduce the amount of fossil fuels that you use every time you walk or ride a bike instead of riding in a car. By choosing not to use a straw in your drink, you reduce the amount of plastic you use.

Reducing

Insulation helps save energy. It keeps a house warm in the winter and cool in the summer.

11. What does reducing mean?

_____

_____

12. Complete the chart about reducing.

Action	What Is Reduced
	amount of fossil fuels used
Increasing window or wall insulation	
drinking without a straw	

13. What does *reusing* mean?

_____

_____

14. Tell how gardeners reuse milk cartons.

_____

_____

Reusing

These containers and cloth diapers can be used over and over again.

Reusing is another way to conserve resources. Reusing can be as simple as using a glass cup again and again instead of throwing away a paper cup after one use.

Reusing also means putting old things to new uses. Gardeners use old milk cartons as planters for starting seeds. They save money because they do not buy new planters. The milk cartons are put to use rather than put in the trash.

You can help save resources for the future by practicing the three R's of conservation.

New Products from Old

Scientists are always looking for ways to reuse and recycle products.

Many companies use a material that looks like wood, but is really recycled plastic. This plastic product is used in fences, decks, outdoor furniture, and many other items. It lasts much longer than wood.

Some construction companies are using recycled glass to pave roads. Broken glass is used in asphalt mixtures. It is in such small pieces that it does not damage tires. It helps to improve road traction.

Recycling

Plastic bottles are sorted at a recycling center. They will be used to make new products.

15. What does *recycling* mean?

_____

_____

_____

16. Put a check mark next to each object that can be made from recycled plastic.

_____ fences

_____ cooking pans

_____ outdoor furniture

_____ pencils

_____ decks

17. What is one use for recycled glass?

_____

_____

_____

Summary Many of Earth's resources are nonrenewable. That means that they cannot be easily replaced. List three ways to conserve resources.

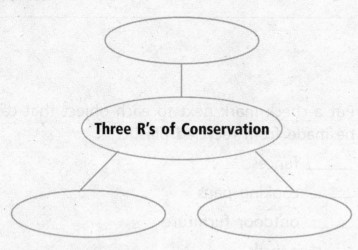

Three R's of Conservation

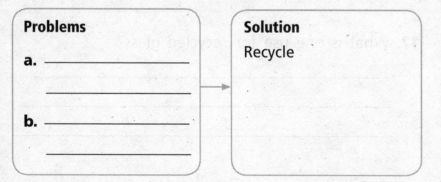

Problem and Solution What problems does using recycled materials help to solve?

Problems	Solution
a. _____	Recycle
_____	
b. _____	
_____	

312

Plastic bottles can be used to make a fleece jacket! The bottles are ground into small pieces, melted, cut, and dyed. All these products help to conserve resources and improve people's lives.

Some people think practicing the three R's of conservation takes too much time or costs too much money. But these examples show that the benefits outweigh the drawbacks.

Plastic bottles can be recycled to make clothing and backpacks.

PROBLEM AND SOLUTION

What problems does using recycled materials help solve?

What Material Resources Are Renewable?

2

Renewable resources can be used again and again, but they must be conserved and used wisely.

Air

The air you breathe is one important example of a renewable resource. Every day, humans and other animals take in oxygen from the air and add carbon dioxide. Green plants and algae do just the opposite. Gases in the air are recycled and renewed.

But the amount of carbon dioxide has been increasing over the past 100 years. There are other unwanted materials in the air we breathe. Particles in the air mix with water in the presence of sunlight and form smog. Smog is not healthy to breathe.

The Clean Air Act limits the pollutants from new cars. Car exhaust must be tested in most states, including California.

VOCABULARY

humus decayed plant and animal material found in soil *(noun)*

soil a natural resource made up of minerals and small rocks, water, gases, and organic matter *(noun)*

topsoil the dark uppermost layer of Earth's soil *(noun)*

VOCABULARY SKILL: Prefixes/Suffixes

In this lesson, you will learn about how pollutants affect renewable resources. The word *pollutant* has the suffix *-ant*, which means "one connected with." The base word *pollute* means "to contaminate." Use these meanings to write a definition for the word *pollutant*.

_____

_____

6.b. Students know that energy and material resources can be classified as renewable or nonrenewable.
6.c. Students know where materials used to make common objects come from in nature.

313

1. What is a renewable resource?

_____

_____

2. Complete the diagram about acid rain.

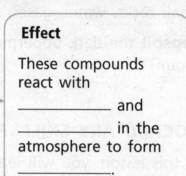

Cause	Effect
Burning fuels release compounds of _____ and _____.	These compounds react with _____ and _____ in the atmosphere to form _____.

3. Tell how landforms and weather patterns affect air pollution over a city.

_____

_____

_____

Los Angeles has some days with clear skies and some days of badly polluted air.

Many fuels release compounds of nitrogen and sulfur when they are burned. These compounds react with water and oxygen in the atmosphere to form acid rain.

Cities usually have the worst air pollution. This is because there are many factories, cars, trucks, and other devices that burn fuels in cities.

Some cities are near landforms such as mountains. Landforms and weather patterns can make air pollution worse. Polluted air gets "trapped" over a city.

Humans do not cause all air pollution. Wildfires or volcanic eruptions can release huge amounts of smoke and soot into the air.

4. Tell how air pollution harms people's health.

_____

_____

_____

I Wonder . . . What is being done to reduce air pollution?

_____

_____

_____

Air pollution can harm people's health. Pollutants get trapped in the lungs. They can cause diseases. Plants and animals can suffer, too.

The government has set strict standards for cars, factories, and power plants to help prevent air pollution. The Clean Air Act limits the pollutants from cars. Hybrid cars, which run on gas and electricity, are becoming more popular.

Air Quality Index	
0 – 50	Good
51 – 100	Moderate
101 – 150	Unhealthy for sensitive groups
151 – 200	Unhealthy
201 – 300	Very unhealthy
301 – 500	Hazardous

The air quality index measures air pollution.

5. Rewrite the statement to make it *true*.

Freshwater is a nonrenewable resource that sometimes results from the water cycle.

_____

_____

6. (Circle) the percentage of Earth's water that is salt water. Draw a box around the percentage of Earth's water that is freshwater that people can use.

1%   50%   65%   88%   97%

Freshwater

Freshwater is another renewable resource. Water is constantly being renewed through the water cycle.

Most of Earth's surface is covered by water, but 97 percent of the water is salt water. Salt water cannot be used for drinking or for plants and crops.

Less than 1 percent of Earth's water is freshwater that people can use. This freshwater is not spread evenly over Earth. People in many places struggle to find safe drinking water.

Much of the freshwater supply is used to water crops.

Less than 1 percent of Earth's surface water is drinkable.

There are many recreational uses for Earth's freshwater.

At one time, the Chicago River was so polluted that fish couldn't live in it. It is now home to 50 fish species and ducks, herons, and beavers.

Much of Earth's freshwater supply is in rivers, streams, ponds, lakes, and wetlands. People use freshwater for irrigation, or watering crops. Freshwater is also needed for drinking, cooking, bathing, and other everyday uses.

Everyone must help keep Earth's freshwater clean and usable. Factories must not dump chemicals into bodies of water. Farmers must not let pesticides and fertilizers run into lakes, rivers, and streams. Landfills must be lined to keep pollutants out of groundwater.

7. List four uses of freshwater.

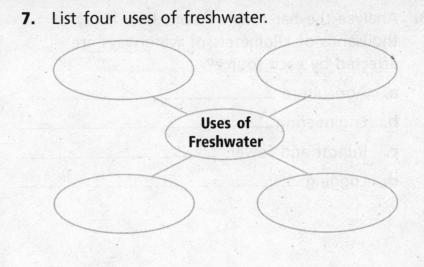

Uses of Freshwater

8. Explain how people can help keep Earth's freshwater clean and usable.

a. Factories _____
_____.

b. Farmers _____
_____.

c. Landfills _____
_____.

9. Analyze the bar graph. About how many thousands of kilometers of waterways are affected by each source?

a. Agriculture _____

b. Engineering _____

c. Runoff and Sewers _____

d. Logging _____

10. (Circle) the most important water source in Southern California.

Mississippi River

Colorado River

Ohio River

Missouri River

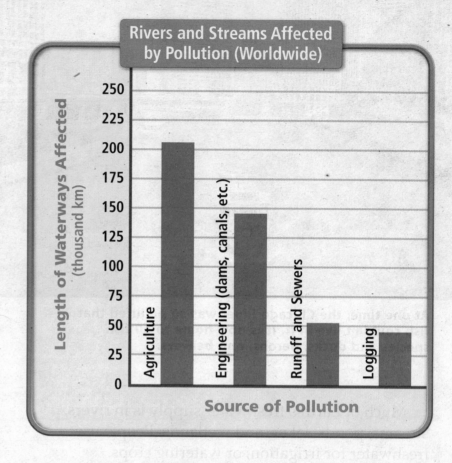

Rivers and Streams Affected by Pollution (Worldwide)

Water Sources

Most communities have a system for providing water to residents. Water may be drawn from nearby lakes or rivers or pumped from groundwater wells. Sometimes water is brought in from other places.

A watershed provides 85 percent of the water in the San Francisco Bay area. Snowmelt fills rivers and collects in reservoirs, or holding places. In Southern California, the Colorado River is an important source of water.

Soil

Soil is a natural resource made up of minerals, small rocks, water, gases, and organic matter. It is a renewable resource. The organic matter in soil, called **humus** (HYOO muhs), is decayed plant and animal material.

Soil is different in different places. Factors that affect soil include climate, types of rock that form the soil, and the area's plants and animals. Different types of soil hold water differently. Sandy soil dries quickly. Clay soil holds more water.

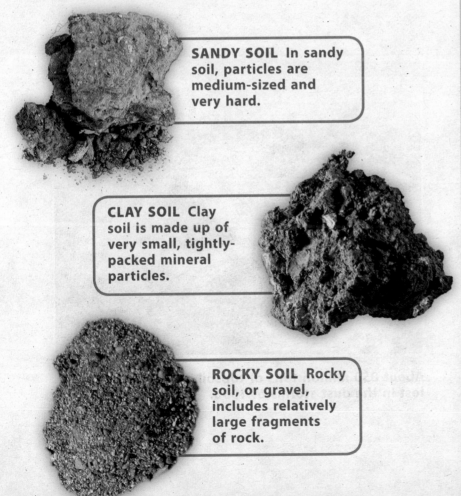

SANDY SOIL In sandy soil, particles are medium-sized and very hard.

CLAY SOIL Clay soil is made up of very small, tightly-packed mineral particles.

ROCKY SOIL Rocky soil, or gravel, includes relatively large fragments of rock.

---

11. Put a check mark next to materials that make up soil.

_____ organic matter

_____ cloth

_____ water

_____ small rocks

_____ logs

_____ boulders

_____ gases

12. Complete the chart about types of soil.

Soil Type	Clues
	• gravel • large fragments of rock
	• medium-sized, hard particles • dries quickly
	• holds water • small, tightly-packed mineral particles

319

13. List the organisms that break down organic matter in soil.

a. _____

b. _____

c. _____

d. _____

14. Complete the diagram about what makes up topsoil.

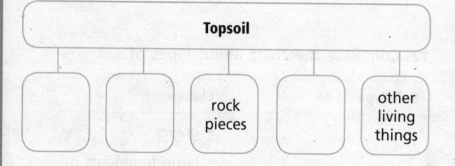

Soil is home to many living things. Bacteria live in soil. The bacteria help break down the organic matter in soil, recycling it for plants to use again. This is also done by fungi, algae, and protists. Earthworms and some insects help the process.

The dark, uppermost layer of Earth's soil is called **topsoil**. Topsoil contains humus, minerals, rock pieces, bacteria, and other living things. Topsoil has more nutrients than other layers of soil. Plants need nutrients in the same way your body needs vitamins and minerals.

About 850 million tons of topsoil were lost in the dust storms of 1935.

Crop rotation helps to restore nutrients to the soil.

Topsoil must be protected from erosion by wind and water. If topsoil is not protected, it can easily erode.

Wind breaks are lines of fences or trees that protect the soil from the wind. Contour farming is a way of planting crops to protect the soil from water erosion.

Farmers plant different crops during different growing seasons. The plants take up different nutrients from the soil. Some plants return nutrients to the soil. This is called crop rotation. Farmers also use fertilizers to return nutrients to the soil.

15. Identify how topsoil can be protected from wind and water erosion.

Way to Protect Topsoil	Clue
	• protects soil from water erosion
	• planting different crops during different growing seasons to return nutrients to the soil
	• line of fences or trees that protects a field from wind

16. Forests are important to life on Earth because they provide _____.

17. Complete the diagram about products made from trees.

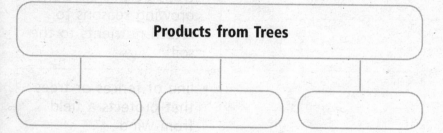

Forests

Forests are very important to life on Earth because trees are a major source of oxygen.

Trees are used to make products that you use every day. Almost every paper product you can think of comes from trees. Trees also provide lumber to build homes and to make furniture. Wood from trees can be burned as fuel.

Trees are planted, grown, and cut down just like any other crop. Some trees are cut down in natural forests. Trees in national parks like Sequoia National Park are protected.

Trees are a valuable natural resource.

At a paper mill, wood pulp is processed into long, wide sheets.

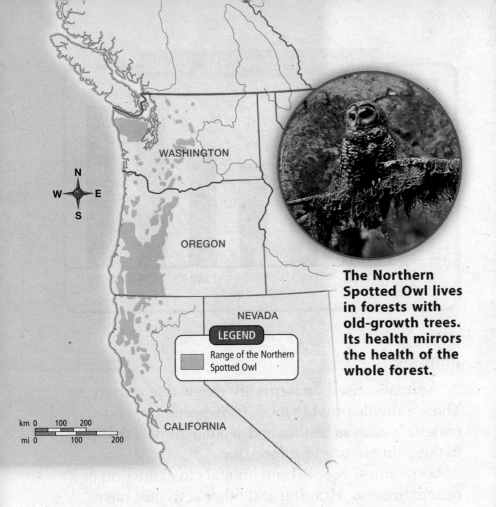

The Northern Spotted Owl lives in forests with old-growth trees. Its health mirrors the health of the whole forest.

Forests and Wildlife

Tropical rain forests once covered huge areas of land in South America, Africa, and other places near the equator. Now these forests are being cut down.

Rain forests are important because they are home to more species than any other place on Earth. When rain forests are cut down, these animals lose their home. Many species become extinct.

Cutting down Earth's forests is just one example of how humans are affecting other species.

18. Complete the diagram about the relationship between rain forests and wildlife.

Cause		Effect
Rain forests are cut down by humans.	→	Animals _____ their homes and may become _____.

19. Circle the area in California where the Northern Spotted Owl lives.

323

Summary   Renewable resources can be used again and again. Even so, they should be conserved and used wisely. Animals are a renewable resource. List three ways that animals are used.

a. _____

b. _____

c. _____

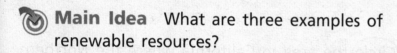 **Main Idea** What are three examples of renewable resources?

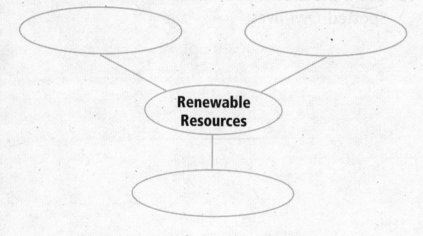

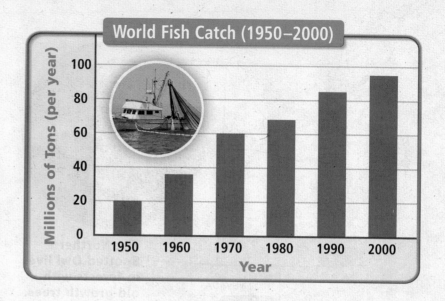

World Fish Catch (1950–2000)

Animals

Animals raised on farms are renewable resources. These animals provide food, transportation, and materials such as leather and wool. Animals that live in the wild are used for food, too.

Sometimes, people hunt animals to extinction or near extinction. Hunting and other activities have caused populations of native wildlife to go down. Cows, sheep, chickens, and other animals are taking their place. Earth no longer has as many different animals as it once did.

Zoos used to be a place for entertainment only. Now, many zoos may be the last home for many animal species.

MAIN IDEA

What are three examples of renewable resources?

humus (HYOO muhs) decayed plant and animal
material found in soil

   humus animales y plantas descompuestos que
   se hallan en el suelo

material resource things from Earth that can be used to make
new products

   recursos materiales cosas de la Tierra que pueden usarse para
   fabricar productos nuevos

mineral a solid crystalline chemical element or
compound that occurs naturally in Earth's crust

   mineral elemento o compuesto químico sólido
   cristalino que se da de forma natural en la naturaleza

ore a rock that contains enough of a useful mineral to make it valuable

   mena roca que contiene suficiente mineral metalífero para que
   sea útil

recycling recovering a resource from one item and
using that resource to make another item

   reciclar recuperar un recurso utilizando un objeto
   viejo para fabricar un objeto nuevo

soil a natural resource made up of minerals and small
rocks, water, gases, and organic matter

   tierra recurso natural compuesto de minerales y trozos de roca, agua,
   gases y materia orgánica

topsoil the dark uppermost layer of Earth's soil

   capa superficial la primera capa oscura de la Tierra

Visit www.eduplace.com to play puzzles
and word games.

Write a short paragraph using the words on the
page.

_____

_____

_____

_____

Circle the words in this Glossary that are the
same in English and Spanish.

Chapter Review

WHAT DID YOU LEARN?

Vocabulary

❶ (Circle) the correct answer on the page.

Comprehension

❷ _____

_____

❸ _____

_____

_____

❹ _____

_____

_____

Critical Thinking

❺ _____

_____

_____

Think About What You Have Read

Vocabulary

❶ The layer of soil in which plants grow is _____.

A) topsoil

B) mineral

C) ore

D) humus

Comprehension

❷ What benefits and drawbacks come from shipping resources around the world?

❸ Why is water conservation important?

❹ Why are Earth's forests important resources?

Critical Thinking

❺ Design a plan to conserve material resources that can be used by your family. It should be practical and involve the reducing, reusing, and recycling of materials.

Index